Everyone is right, everything is wrong;
Don't let the changes get you down, man.
Everyone is wrong, everything is all right now;
Don't let the changes get you uptight.

From "Changes" by Donovan Leitch (Ireland).

NEW WORLDS

NEW WORLDS AHEAD

NEW WORLDS OF READING

NEW WORLDS OF LITERATURE

NEW WORLDS OF IDEAS

NEW WORLD ISSUES

Together

Currents

♦ Changes

Mix

Teacher's Manual or Teacher's Edition
and Reader's Notebook or Writer's Journal
for Each Anthology

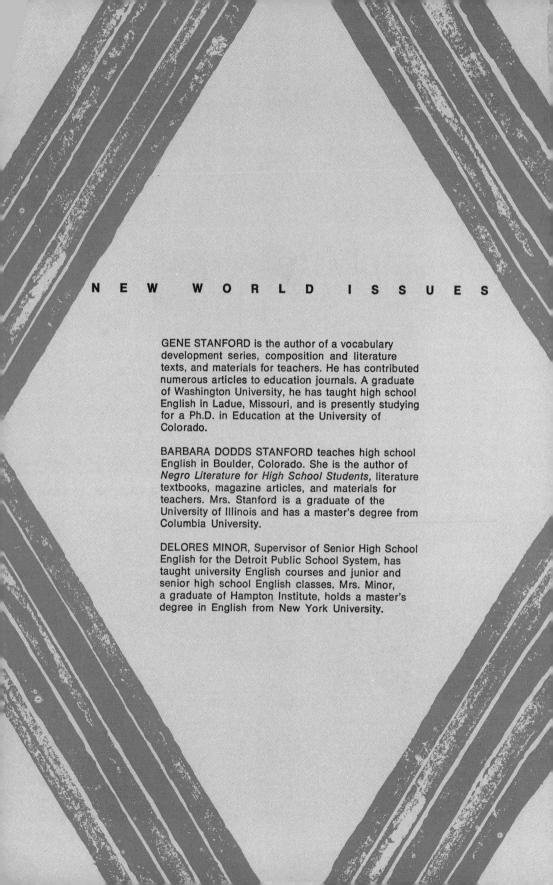

N E W   W O R L D   I S S U E S

GENE STANFORD is the author of a vocabulary
development series, composition and literature
texts, and materials for teachers. He has contributed
numerous articles to education journals. A graduate
of Washington University, he has taught high school
English in Ladue, Missouri, and is presently studying
for a Ph.D. in Education at the University of
Colorado.

BARBARA DODDS STANFORD teaches high school
English in Boulder, Colorado. She is the author of
Negro Literature for High School Students, literature
textbooks, magazine articles, and materials for
teachers. Mrs. Stanford is a graduate of the
University of Illinois and has a master's degree from
Columbia University.

DELORES MINOR, Supervisor of Senior High School
English for the Detroit Public School System, has
taught university English courses and junior and
senior high school English classes. Mrs. Minor,
a graduate of Hampton Institute, holds a master's
degree in English from New York University.

CHANGES

GENE STANFORD

BARBARA DODDS STANFORD

Consultant
Delores Minor

HARCOURT BRACE JOVANOVICH, INC.

New York   Chicago   San Francisco   Atlanta   Dallas

ACKNOWLEDGMENTS: *For permission to reprint copyrighted material, grateful
acknowledgment is made to the following sources:*

ABELARDO DIAZ ALFARO: " 'Santa Clo' comes to La Cuchilla" by Abelardo Díaz Alfaro, translated
by Julio de la Torre.
A. S. BARNES & COMPANY, INC.: "Song of a Mother to Her First-Born" from "Song of a Mother to
Her First-Born" translated by Jack H. Driberg from *Initiation* by Jack H. Driberg. Published by
Golden Cockerel Press.
OLUMBE BASSIR: "Forefathers" by Birago Diop from *Anthology of West African Verse* by
Olumbe Bassir.
ALBERT AND CHARLES BONI, INC.: "Love of One's Neighbor" by Leonid Andreyev, translated by
Thomas Seltzer from *15 International One-Act Plays*, the condensed and revised edition from
Voice, March 16, 1970.
CHERRY LANE MUSIC CO.: "What Did You Learn in School Today?" by Tom Paxton, copyright
© 1962, 1964, 1965 by Cherry Lane Music Co. All Rights Reserved.
CITY LIGHTS BOOKS: "The Dunce" from *Selections from Paroles* by Jacques Prévert, translated by
Lawrence Ferlinghetti, copyright © 1947 by Les Editions du Point du Jour.
CROWN PUBLISHERS, INC.: "The Bench" from "The Bench" by Richard Rive from *An African
Treasury*, edited by Langston Hughes, © 1960 by Langston Hughes.
DELL PUBLISHING CO., INC.: "A Letter to God" by Gregorio López y Fuentes, translated by Don-
ald A. Yates from *Great Spanish Short Stories* by Angel Flores. Copyright © 1962 by Dell Pub-
lishing Company, Inc.
LANDON GERALD DOWDEY: "The Fool" by Padraic Pearse as adapted by Landon Gerald Dowdey
© 1969 in *Journey to Freedom* (Swallow).
E. P. DUTTON & CO., INC.: "Nobody Home" from the book *Triquarterly Anthology of Contemporary Latin American Literature* edited by José Donoso and William A. Henkin, copyright ©
1939 by Triquarterly, Northwestern University Press. Published by E. P. Dutton & Co., Inc.
EDITIONS SEGHERS: "Leaf in the Wind" by Bernard B. Dadié from *A Book of African Verse*,
edited by J. Reed and C. Wake, published in 1964.
FARRAR, STRAUS & GIROUX, INC.: From *The Dark Child* by Camara Laye, copyright 1954 by Ca-
mara Laye. "My Voice" by Juan Ramón Jiménez, translated by H. R. Hays from *Selected Writ-
ings of Juan Ramón Jiménez*, copyright © 1957 by Juan Ramón Jiménez.
FREDERICK FELL, INC., *386 Park Avenue South, New York, N.Y. 10016*: "The Bridge" by Nicolai
Chukovski and "The Two Kinds of Truth" by Pyotr Zamoyski from *Treasury of Russian Short
Stories 1900–1966*, translated by Selig O. Wassner, copyright 1968 by Selig O. Wassner.
GROVE PRESS, INC.: Adapted from Scene 1 from *The 400 Blows* by François Truffaut, translated
by David Denby, copyright © 1969 by Grove Press, Inc., copyright © 1959 by Zenith International
Film Corporation. Adapted from *The Wretched of the Earth* by Frantz Fanon, translated from the
French by Constance Farrington, copyright © 1963 by Presence Africaine.
GROVE PRESS, INC. and METHUEN & CO. LTD.: From *A Taste of Honey* by Shelagh Delaney, copy-
right © 1959 by Theatre Workshop (Pioneer Theatres Ltd.).
HARCOURT BRACE JOVANOVICH, INC.: "The Brave Man of Golo" from *The King's Drum*, copyright
© 1962 by Harold Courlander. "A Worker Reads History" from *Selected Poems of Bertolt
Brecht*, translated by H. R. Hays, copyright, 1947, by Bertolt Brecht and H. R. Hays.
HARPER & ROW, PUBLISHERS, INC.: "Fool's Paradise" from *Zlateh The Goat and Other Stories*
by Isaac Bashevis Singer, copyright © 1966 by Isaac Bashevis Singer. Abridgment of "Who
Cares" (pp. 37–50, retitled "Janaki") from *Gifts of Passage* by Santha Rama Rau, copyright ©
1958 by Vasanthi Rama Rau Bowers.
HARPER & ROW, PUBLISHERS, INC. and PETER OWEN LTD.: Abridged from pp. 5–6, 9–11, 12–18
Demian by Hermann Hesse, translated from the German by Michael Roloff and Michael Lebeck,
copyright 1925 by S. Fischer Verlag; copyright © 1965 by Harper & Row, Publishers, Inc.
Demian by Hermann Hesse is published in Canada by Peter Owen, London.
HARPER & ROW, PUBLISHERS, INC.: "Tuesday Siesta" from *No One Writes To The Colonel and
Other Stories* by Gabriel Garcia-Marquez. Translated from the Spanish by J. S. Bernstein,
copyright © 1968 in the English translation by Harper & Row, Publishers, Inc.
INDIANA UNIVERSITY PRESS: "Once Upon a Time" by Gabriel Okara from *Poems from Black
Africa*, edited by Langston Hughes, copyright © 1963 by Langston Hughes.

Research at Harcourt Brace Jovanovich:

PHYLLIS GOLDENBERG   ALAN PETRASKE   MADELINE TRAVERS

MURRAY FLEMINGER

Contents

That's what I learned in school (U.S.A.)   51

Our baby's gone (England) 89

Look what they done to my song (U.S.A.)   117

What if the dream came true? (Ireland)   161

Do what you've never done before (Ireland)   193

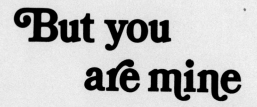

But you are mine

Someone would like to have you for her child
but you are mine.
Someone would like to rear you on a costly mat
but you are mine.
Someone would like to place you on a camel blanket
but you are mine.
I have you to rear on a torn old mat.
Someone would like to have you as her child
but you are mine.

From "Lullaby," Akan traditional (Ghana).

from Prayer Before Birth

LOUIS MAC NEICE

I am not yet born; O hear me.
Let not the bloodsucking bat or the rat or the stoat or the
    clubfooted ghoul come near me.

I am not yet born; console me.
I fear that the human race may with tall walls wall me,
    with strong drugs dope me, with wise lies lure me,
        on black racks rack me, in blood baths roll me.

I am not yet born; provide me
With water to dandle me, grass to grow for me, trees to talk
    to me, sky to sing to me, birds and a white light
        in the back of my mind to guide me.

SONG OF A MOTHER
TO HER FIRST-BORN

SUDANESE TRADITIONAL

O my child, now indeed I am happy.
Now indeed I am a wife—
No more a bride, but a Mother-of-one.
Be splendid and magnificent, child of desire.
Be proud as I am proud.

Be happy as I am happy.
Be loved as now I am loved.
Child, child, child, love I have had from my man.
But now, only now, have I the fullness of love.
Now, only now, am I his wife and the mother of his first-born.
His soul is safe in your keeping, my child, and it was I, I, I who have
    made you.

Therefore am I loved.
Therefore am I happy.
Therefore am I a wife.
Therefore have I great honor.

You will tend his shrine when he is gone.
With sacrifice and oblation you will recall his name year by year.
He will live in your prayers, my child,
And there will be no more death for him, but everlasting life
    springing from your loins.
You are his shield and his spear, his hope and redemption from the
    dead.
Through you he will be reborn, as the saplings in the Spring.
And I, I am the mother of his first-born.
Sleep, child of beauty and courage and fulfillment, sleep.
I am content.

Translated by Jack H. Driberg

We had left Paris because there was a war on and we were Jewish. My father was from Poland and my mother was from Rumania. They were furriers. They loved each other and I was born. I was happy. I did whatever I liked and I was always getting in trouble. It was wonderful. When he talked about me, my father would throw up his hands as from **The Two of Us**

CLAUDE BERRI

if to say there was nothing he could do and my mother would smile at his confusion as if she had played a good trick on him by bringing me into the world. I was happy. So were my parents. In spite of all the trouble I caused them, and even though we were poor. But they loved each other and they loved me. And there were always friends in the house.

One day my father spoke to me in a voice that I had never heard before, a voice that came from very far away. His face was handsomer than usual and his eyes were tenderer. He told me that I would have to be good now. Because there was a war on, and because we were Jewish.

My mother talked to me too. She told me that war was a terrible thing and that to be Jewish when there was a war was even more terrible. That I would have to be good. Because otherwise she might die and so might Papa. I did not want my parents to die. I cried. I promised to be good. As good as gold. As good as the smartest kid in class, whom I couldn't stand. Because I was Jewish and because there was a war on.

Unfortunately, I wasn't used to being good.

School was over. A German soldier was lounging in front of a shop window. Huddled in our hooded capes, Tiberius and I were planning our escapade. Our minds were made up; we would do it today. For days we had been dreaming about a tank we had seen in the toy department of the dime store on *Rue Voltaire*. Tiberius kept watch. I did the rest. The next thing we knew, we were at the police station.

The tank sat in state on the desk of the chief of police. We were terrified. We couldn't tell whether the police chief's smile was mean or nice. We were hiding under our capes. Tiberius was crying. I was beyond tears. The clock struck six and it was like being hit in the stomach. The police chief lit a match and it was an explosion. I thought about my parents.

Tiberius's father arrived first and pounced on his son. Now I was alone. The police chief toyed with the tank. He looked at the time. I decided he was in a hurry and I told myself that there was hope. My father came in. I threw him a desperate look. He showed his papers, and I heard the police chief say that I was a troublemaker.

I took my father's hand. He squeezed my hand very hard and I noticed that he was trembling. A German patrol marched by. Their steps were loud in the stillness of the night.

We lived in a room which we used as bedroom, kitchen, and furrier's shop. A candelabra with seven candlesticks cast a faint light on the whitewashed walls. My father was spanking me. My mother was crying. The dressmaker's dummy seemed to understand. I was very unhappy. I was sorry for what I had done. I promised myself that I would be good and I accepted my punishment without a word. When it was over I pulled up my pants.

"A public nuisance."

My father threw up his hands in that gesture of helplessness which usually made my mother smile.

"A real public nuisance. . . . How long is this going to go on? . . . How long? . . . For a tank. For a tank we could all have gotten caught."

6

He sank into a chair and put his face in his hands. He looked so unhappy that I wanted to console him.

"Calm yourself. Eat," my mother told him.

"I'm not hungry. Your son has given me a bellyful."

I was hungry. Ravenously I drank the soup which my mother fed me with a spoon. It was salty from the tears I couldn't hold back.

There was a silence, which made me feel better. Then my father moaned like a wounded animal.

"How long are you going to go on feeding him with a spoon?"

To prove my good will, I took the spoon out of my mother's hands. My father tried not to smile. He sat down next to me and talked to me in a gentle voice.

"Do you want to get us all arrested? Is that what you want? Is our life too safe for you? It's not enough to be afraid of the postman or the milkman? Afraid of being turned in for a yes or a no? You think we have to attract more attention by stealing tanks? You think it's not enough as it is? You think we don't have enough troubles?"

I ate my soup all by myself and I listened as seriously as I could.

"Why did you do it? . . . Do you want us to die?"

I put my arms around his neck. The idea that he could die and that it might be my fault terrified me. He took me in his arms. My mother cleared the table. She left my father's plate. Sooner or later, he always ate.

"You think we don't make enough sacrifices for you? Didn't I give you a fire engine, Indians, private lessons in math and spelling? We don't make enough sacrifices for you? You have to have a tank yet?"

I had cried myself out. I couldn't keep my eyes open. My mother handed me my pajamas. She didn't have to rock me that night.

"What's so good about a tank, anyway?"

He always had the last word. And on this word I fell asleep.

A nightmare woke me up. I was afraid, but I didn't wake my parents. A ray of moonlight came through the window and made a little light in the room. My father and mother were sleeping with their arms around each other, as if to give each other courage. They were very beautiful. I said to myself that I loved them, and it was the first time I was aware of it. Usually I never thought about it, or else it was because I thought about it all the time. I don't know. This thought consoled me and I wasn't afraid any more. I went over and kissed them very softly. So they wouldn't wake up. Then I went back to bed.

I adored Mickey the Tailor. No sadness could hold out against a story about Mickey the Tailor. For a story about Mickey the Tailor I was capable of doing my homework ahead of time, taking down the garbage, running races, even eating turnips. Mickey the Tailor made me good again. I loved him. He was part of my life. If he had walked into the house one day, I wouldn't have been surprised. This had been going on for years. My father had exhausted all the resources of the character. He had served Mickey the Tailor with every possible sauce. With him he had told me about his childhood in Poland, the sleighs, the white plains, growing up in Paris, his friends, his struggles, how he met my mother, and how they fell in love.

Because of Mickey the Tailor I knew all about loyalty, love, and tenderness. Through him I had learned about the seriousness of friendship, the necessity for courage, the joy of accomplishment, and the uncertainty of power. He had taught me to notice the smells of the country, the ray of sunlight on the table while my mother ironed—busy little bee that she was. What others have learned from books or from life itself, Mickey the Tailor taught me through the magic of a father's love for his child.

"Mickey the Tailor had a son like you . . . who wouldn't eat his turnips without being coaxed . . . who wouldn't mind his papa and his mama . . . a son who gave him a lot of aggravation. . . . Mickey the Tailor didn't know what to do with his son . . . to make his son behave, to make him understand the situation."

"Was Mickey the Tailor Jewish?"

"Of course."

"And his son too?"

"Of course."

I ate my turnips and listened gravely. My father looked happy. I imagine he must have been counting on Mickey the Tailor to make me understand "the situation," as he called it, once and for all.

"There was a war on and Mickey the Tailor's son refused to understand the situation . . . refused to understand that he must come right home after school . . . that he couldn't play outside . . . that he must be good . . . learn to eat by himself . . . to wash by himself . . . to make his own bed . . . to help his mother a little. . . . Mickey the Tailor didn't know what to do to make his son understand. When he was nice to his son, his son was bad. When he was mean to his son, his son was bad too. . . ."

Mickey the Tailor had helped me to understand. That night when I went to bed I promised myself that I would really be good. The war wouldn't last forever. And I would have to be patient. Later I would play. I was sad, but my mind was made up. Besides, I was sure that Mickey the Tailor would help me be good. My parents kissed me. Then they went to visit their friend Raymonde who lived down the hall. I went to sleep.

The sirens woke me up. Their wail terrified me. I lay paralyzed in my bed, unable to move a muscle or utter a sound. If somebody had cut my heart out with a knife, I wouldn't have bled.

My mother ran into the room and picked me up. Silently I pressed myself against the warmth of her body, and this made me feel better.

A ray of moonlight streamed through the air shaft and lit the cellar. In the distance, bombs were falling. Some of the women were praying. Others were weeping. Some were very brave. The men were talking about the war. Some said it would soon be over. Others said it would be long. I agreed with the first. I convinced myself that they were right. That way I could play in peace.

I wasn't afraid. My father and mother were there. When I was with them I felt that nothing could happen to me. They were calm. Their friend Raymonde was with them. Her face had lines in it but it was beautiful. I liked her because my parents did. A cat jumped into my lap and I petted it. The scream of the sirens announced the all clear and my blood froze again.

I buried my face in my mother's neck until the noise had stopped. Outside the night was clear and we all went back to our homes.

Because my parents were worried about me, Raymonde had offered to take me to the country to stay with her father, who was a fine old man. My parents had accepted.

The thought of leaving my parents was unbearable. I didn't go out to play the last few days before my departure. I didn't feel like it. I stayed with my parents. I wanted to make the most of the little time I had left. But I understood. I hadn't complained. I was a man now. I gritted my teeth. I didn't let them see me cry. I did it secretly. I went inside the toilet, but not to smoke cigarettes made of chestnut leaves. I cried silently so as not to attract attention. Then I went and washed my face at the tap in the courtyard.

My parents told me that the country was beautiful down there. They said that I would be happy, and that they would come and get me when the war was over. And that afterward we would be happy all the time. They congratulated me on my courage, and told me that Mickey the Tailor would have been proud of me.

The train was there and my heart was heavy. It was raining in Caluires and it was cold. It was January. The German soldiers made green spots in the crowd. The people were sad. I told myself that when I grew up I would never go to war, and that if everybody else did the same, there wouldn't be any little boys on station platforms saying good-by to their parents.

In the compartment Raymonde was looking after the baggage. I was on the platform with my parents. My mother stared straight ahead as if she were afraid to look at me, afraid she would lose her courage. My father took me in his arms.

"Do you know your name?"

"Yes, Papa: Claude Longet."

"No. Not Longet . . . Longuet . . . understand? . . . Longuet . . . Longuet. . . . It's easy!"

"Yes, Papa."

"How do you spell Longuet?"

"L . . . O . . . N . . . G . . . E. . . ."

My father put me down and threw up his hands, the way he always did when he didn't understand. God knows, I had given him enough opportunities not to understand. I really was a funny kid.

Some German soldiers walked right by us. My mother bent down.

"Pay attention, my darling. . . . It says Longuet on your ration book. . . . Longuet."

I burst into tears. They were asking too much of me. It was hard enough being brave. . . . If I had to learn to spell too! I fought back my tears. My father took over. My mother stared ahead of her again to keep from breaking down.

"At your age, you have to know your name!"

"Yes, but it isn't my name."

"Until the end of the war, it is your name, do you understand?" The people were hurrying. It was almost time. A voice rang out over the loudspeaker.

"All passengers for the train to Grenoble . . . Please get on board."

My mother took me in her arms and hugged me so hard it hurt.

"After the war, will I have my own name back?"

"Yes, my darling. After the war your name will be Langmann again forever . . . forever. . . ."

Her voice sounded funny. She put me in my father's arms and stared ahead of her again. My father walked toward the door to the car.

"Do you remember the prayer Raymonde taught you?"

"Yes, Papa."

I mustered all the courage I had left and murmured, "Our Father which art in heaven, hallowed be thy name . . . thy kingdom come . . . thy will be done, on earth as it is in heaven. . . ."

He set me down on the steps of the train.

"Give us . . ." I stopped. I couldn't go on. My father looked at me pleadingly.

"Give us what?"

I told myself that I'd have plenty of time to practice the prayer on the train. I said, "Kiss me."

He kissed me. Then Raymonde came and took me into the compartment.

I was standing at the window of the compartment, holding my head in my hands. My father and mother had their arms around each other. They only had each other now and they were paralyzed with grief. They looked very beautiful and I thought how much I loved them. I winked at them to cheer them up. This was when the tears came and the train started to move. Everything happened very fast. I saw my father dash forward. He rummaged in his pockets as he ran and handed me his pocket watch through the window. My mother was standing very straight. My father was panting in time to the train. Then he stopped and saluted me like one man to another. The train whistled. My parents disappeared. I held the pocket watch to my ear and felt as if I were hearing my father's heart beating.

Translated by Helen Weaver

Parents Are Not Payable

AHMAD NASSIR BIN JUMA BHALO

Since I was born   I have never seen clearly
that a human, my friend   has paid his parent
for the pregnancy and the pains   of birth, and the rearing
parents are not payable   even though you may want to pay them.

First they had to put up with   staying awake all night
lifting you up   like a bunch of coconuts
now on this side, now on that   and hushing up your crying
parents are not payable   even though you may want to pay them.

Your mother cleaned you up   and dressed you in baby clothes
to say nothing of your weight   during the nine months of pregnancy
the day you were born   she could scarcely get her breath
parents are not payable   even though you may want to pay them.

Sit down and think   whenever you were unwell
she exercised her wits   until she identified the sickness
so don't deceive yourself   for that will bring you to the slippery path
parents are not payable   even though you may want to pay them.

I will not lie to you   for that is not nice
from the creation of the world   up to the present time
I have never heard   of anyone who has paid a parent
parents are not payable   even though you may want to pay them.

Translated by Lyndon Harries

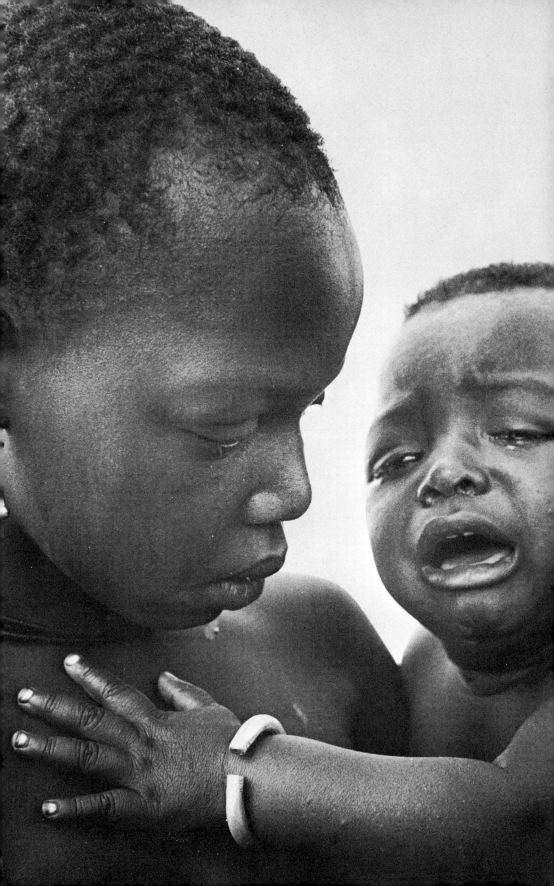

Father Bird and Fledglings

JEWISH TRADITIONAL

We should, I say, put ourselves to great pains for our children, for on this the world is built, yet we must understand that if children did as much for their parents, the children would quickly tire of it.

A bird once set out to cross a windy sea with its three fledglings. The sea was so wide and the wind so strong, the father bird was forced to carry his young, one by one, in his strong claws. When he was halfway across with the first fledgling the wind turned to a gale, and he said, "My child, look how I am struggling and risking my life in your behalf. When you are grown up, will you do as much for me and provide for my old age?"

The fledgling replied, "Only bring me to safety, and when you are old I shall do everything you ask of me."

Whereat the father bird dropped his child into the sea, and it drowned, and he said, "So shall it be done to such a liar as you."

Then the father bird returned to shore, set forth with his second fledgling, asked the same question, and, receiving the same answer, drowned the second child with the cry, "You, too, are a liar."

Finally he set out with the third fledgling, and when he asked the same question, the third and last fledgling replied, "My dear father, it is true you are struggling mightily and risking your life in my behalf, and I shall be wrong not to repay you when you are old, but I cannot bind myself. This though I can promise: when I am grown up and have children of my own, I shall do as much for them as you have done for me."

Whereupon the father bird said, "Well spoken, my child, and wisely: your life I will spare, and I will carry you to shore in safety."

Translated by Marvin Lowenthal

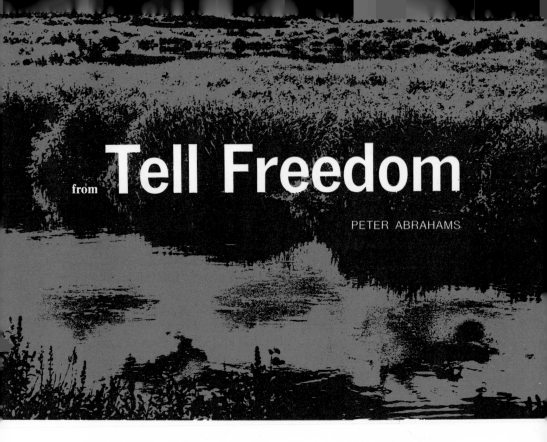

from Tell Freedom

PETER ABRAHAMS

Each day I explored a little more of the river, going farther up or downstream, extending the frontiers of my world. One day, going farther downstream than I had been before, I came upon a boy. He was on the bank on the other side from me. We saw each other at the same time and stared. He was completely naked. He carried two finely carved sticks of equal size and shape, both about his own height. He was not light brown, like the other children of our location, but dark brown, almost black. I moved nearly to the edge of the river. He called out to me in a strange language.

"Hello!" I shouted.

He called out again, and again I could not understand. I searched for a place with stones, then bounded across. I approached him slowly. As I drew near, he gripped his sticks more firmly. I stopped.

He spoke harshly, flung one stick on the ground at my feet, and held the other ready as though to fight.

"Don't want to fight," I said.

I reached down to pick up the stick and return it to him. He took a step forward and raised the one in his hand. I moved back quickly. He stepped back and pointed at the stick on the ground. I shook my head.

"Don't want to fight."

I pushed the stick toward him with my foot, ready to run at the first sign of attack. I showed my new, stubby teeth in a tentative smile. He said something that sounded less aggressive. I nodded, smiling more broadly. He relaxed, picked up the stick, and transferred both to his left hand. He smacked his chest.

"Joseph! Zulu!"

I smacked my own chest. "Lee—" But I didn't know what I was apart from that.

He held out his hand. We shook. His face lit up in a sunny smile. He said something and pointed downstream. Then he took my arm and led me down.

Far downstream, where the river skirted a hillside, hidden by a cluster of willows, we came on a large clear pool. Joseph flung his sticks on the ground and dived in. He shot through the water like a tadpole. He went down and came up. He shouted and beckoned me to come in. I undressed and went in more tentatively. Laughing, he pulled me under. I came up gasping and spluttering, my belly filled with water. He smacked me on the back, and the water shot out of my mouth in a rush. When he realized I could not swim, he became more careful. We spent the afternoon together, with Joseph teaching me to swim.

At home that evening I stood beside Aunt Liza's washtub.

"Aunt Liza—"

"Yes?"

"What am I?"

"What are you talking about?"

"I met a boy at the river. He said he was Zulu."

She laughed.

"You are Colored. There are three kinds of people: white people, Colored people, and black people. The white people come first, then the Colored people, then the black people."

"Why?"

"Because it is so."

Next day when I met Joseph, I smacked my chest and said "Lee! Colored!"

He clapped his hands and laughed.

Joseph and I spent most of the long summer afternoons together. He learned some Afrikaans from me; I learned some Zulu from him. Our days were full.

There was the river to explore.

There were my swimming lessons, and others.

I learned to fight with sticks; to weave a green hat of young willow wands and leaves; to catch frogs and tadpoles with my hands; to set a trap for the *springhaas;* to make the sounds of the river birds.

There was the hot sun to comfort us. . . .

There was the green grass to dry our bodies. . . .

There was the soft clay with which to build. . . .

There was the fine sand with which to fight. . . .

There were our giant grasshoppers to race. . . .

There were the locust swarms, when the skies turned black and we caught them by the hundreds. . . .

There was the rare taste of crisp, brown, baked, salted locusts. . . .

There was the voice of the wind in the willows. . . .

There was the voice of the heavens in thunderstorms. . . .

There were the voices of two children in laughter, ours. . . .

There were Joseph's tales of black kings who lived in days before the white man. . . .

At home, I said, "Aunt Liza—"

"Yes?"

"Did we have Colored kings before the white man?"

"No."

"Then where did we come from? Joseph and his mother come from the black kings who were before the white man."

And laughing, and ruffling my head, she said, "You talk too much. . . . Go'n wash up."

And to Joseph, next day, I said, "We didn't have Colored kings before the white man."

And he comforted me and said, "It is of no moment. You are my brother. Now my kings will be your kings. Come: I have promised the mother to bring you home. She awaits you. I will race you to the hill."

From the top of the hill I looked into a long valley where cattle grazed. To the right, on the sloping land, nestled a cluster of mud huts. Around each hut was a wall built of mud.

"That is my home." Joseph pointed.

We veered right and went down to it. From a distance we saw a woman at the gate of one of the huts.

"There is the mother!" He walked faster.

She was barefooted. She wore a slight shirt that came above her knees. A child was strapped to her back. The upper part of her body was naked except for the cloth across her chest that supported the child. Around her neck, arms, and legs were strings of white beads. As we drew near, I saw that she was young. And her broad, round face was beautiful. Her black eyes were liquid soft. She called out a greeting and smiled. Joseph pushed me forward.

"This is my brother Lee of the Coloreds, little mother."

"Greetings, Mother," I said.

"I greet you, my son," she said softly, a twinkle in her eyes. "As the man of my house has told you, food awaits. Come."

"See!" Joseph puffed out his chest. To his mother he said, "He would not believe when I told him I was the man in our house."

"He is indeed," she said.

Circling the hut was a raised platform. We sat on this while she brought us the food: salted fried locusts, and corn on the cob. She sat near by and watched us eating.

My sixth birthday came. Joseph and the little mother and I celebrated it by the river.

Then, early one morning, just as the first cold touches crept into the morning air, Joseph came to our location.

I was washing up when I heard young voices shouting, "Look at the naked Kaffir! Lee's Kaffir!"

I rushed out. Joseph came gravely to me.

"I come to take leave, my brother. My father has died in the mines, so we go back to our land."

He stood straight and stern, not heeding the shouts of the children about. He was a man. This was the burden of his manhood. I had learned much from him, so I said equally coldly, "I must take leave of the little mother."

"She is a woman. She weeps."

We ran all the way there. . . .

When the little cart had taken them away, I climbed the hill and went down to the river. I carried Joseph's two sticks with me. These were his parting gift to his brother.

"Defend yourself," he had said. "I will make others."

I walked along the river that had been our kingdom. Now it was a desolate place. Joseph had been here with me: now Joseph had gone. Before I realized it, my tears flowed fast. There had been much between us.

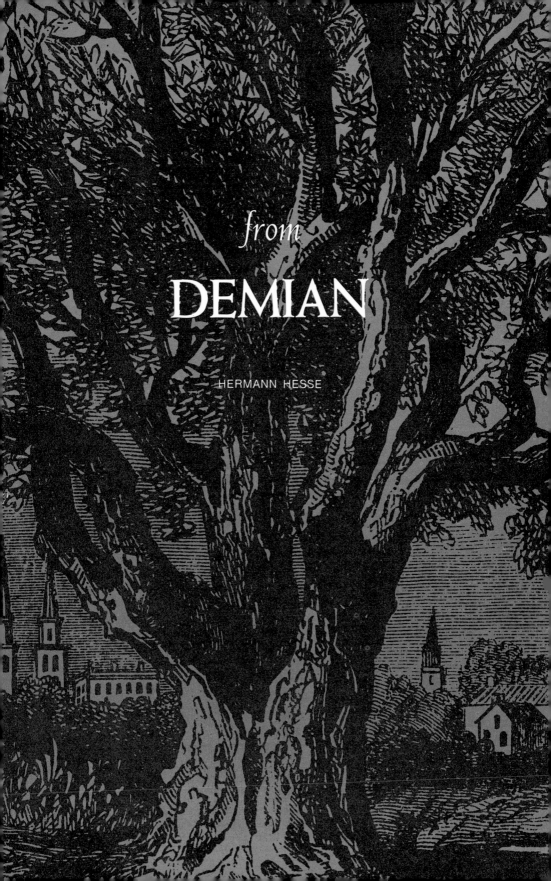

from

DEMIAN

HERMANN HESSE

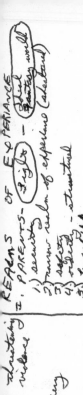

I shall begin my story with an experience I had when I was ten and attended our small town's Latin school.

The realms of day and night, two different worlds coming from two opposite poles, mingled during this time. My parents' house made up one realm, yet its boundaries were even narrower, actually embracing only my parents themselves.

This realm was familiar to me in almost every way—mother and father, love and strictness, model behavior, and school. It was a realm of brilliance, clarity, and cleanliness, gentle conversations, washed hands, clean clothes, and good manners. This was the world in which morning hymns were sung and Christmas celebrated. Straight lines and paths led into the future: there were duty and guilt, bad conscience and confession, forgiveness and good resolutions, love, reverence, wisdom, and the words of the Bible. If one wanted an unsullied and orderly life, one made sure one was in league with this world.

The other realm, however, overlapping half our house, was completely different; it smelled different, spoke a different language, promised and demanded different things. This second world contained servant girls and workmen, ghost stories, rumors of scandal. It was dominated by a loud mixture of horrendous, intriguing, frightful, mysterious things, including slaughterhouses and prisons, drunkards and screeching fishwives, calving cows, horses sinking to their death, tales of robberies, murders, and suicides.

All these wild and cruel, attractive and hideous things surrounded us, could be found in the next alley, the next house. Policemen and tramps, drunkards who beat their wives, droves of young girls pouring out of factories at night, old women who put the hex on you so that you fell ill, thieves hiding in the forest, arsonists nabbed by country police— everywhere this second vigorous world erupted and gave off its scent, everywhere, that is, except in our parents' rooms. And that was good.

It was wonderful that peace and orderliness, quiet and a good conscience, forgiveness and love, ruled in this one realm, and it was wonderful that the rest existed, too, the multitude of harsh noises, of sullenness and violence, from which one could still escape with a leap into one's mother's lap.

II

I attended the Latin school. The mayor's son and the head forester's son were in my class; both visited me at home at times, and though they were quite unruly, they were both members of the good, the legal world. Yet this did not mean that I had no dealings with some of the neighborhood boys who attended public school and on whom we usually looked down. It is with one of them that I must begin my story.

One half-holiday—I was little more than ten years old—two neighborhood kids and I were roaming about when a much bigger boy, a strong and burly kid from public school, the tailor's son, joined us. His father drank and the whole family had a bad name. I had heard much about Franz Kromer, was afraid of him, didn't at all like that he came up to us. His manners were already those of a man and he imitated the walk and speech of young factory workers.

Under his leadership we clambered down the riverbank by the bridge and hid below the first arch. The narrow strip between the vaulted wall of the bridge and the lazily flowing river was covered with nothing but refuse, shards, tangled bundles of rusty wire and other rubbish. Occasionally one could pick up something useful here. Franz Kromer instructed us to comb the area and show him what we found. He would either pocket it or fling it into the river. He put us on the lookout for objects made of lead, brass, and tin, all of which he tucked away—also an old comb made of horn.

I felt very uneasy in his presence, not only because I knew that my father would not have approved of my being seen in his company, but because I was simply afraid of Franz himself, though I was glad that he seemed to accept me and treat me like the others. He gave instructions and we obeyed—it seemed like an old habit, even though this was the first time I was with him.

After a while we sat down. Franz spit into the water, and he looked like a man; he spit through a gap between his teeth and hit whatever he aimed at. A conversation started up, and the boys began boasting and heaping praise on themselves for all sorts of schoolboy heroics and tricks they had played.

I kept quiet and yet was afraid I'd be noticed, that my silence might particularly incur Kromer's wrath. My two friends had begun to shun me the very moment Franz Kromer had joined us. I was a stranger among them and felt that my manners and clothes presented a kind of challenge. As a Latin school boy, the spoiled son of a well-to-do father, it would be impossible for Franz to like me, and the other two, I felt acutely, would soon disown and desert me.

Finally, out of sheer nervousness, I began telling a story too. I invented a long tale about a robbery in which I filled the role of hero. In a garden near the mill, I said, together with a friend I had stolen a whole sackful of apples one night, and by no means ordinary apples but apples of the very best sort.

It was the fear of the moment that made me seek refuge in this story—inventing and telling stories came naturally to me. In order not to fall immediately silent again, and perhaps become involved in something worse, I gave a complete display of my narrative powers. One of us, I continued, had had to stand guard while the other climbed the tree and shook out the apples. Moreover, the sack had grown so heavy that we had to open it again, leaving half the apples behind. But half an hour later we had returned and fetched the rest.

When I had finished I waited for approval of some sort. I had warmed to my subject toward the end and been carried away by my own eloquence. The two younger ones kept silent, waiting, but Franz Kromer looked sharply at me out of narrowed eyes and asked threateningly:

"Is that true?"

"Yes," I said.

"Really and truly?"

"Yes, really and truly," I insisted stubbornly while choking inwardly with fear.

"Would you swear to it?"

I became very afraid but at once said yes.

"Then say: By God and the grace of my soul."

"By God and the grace of my soul," I said.

"Well, all right," he said and turned away.

I thought everything was all right now, and was glad when he got up and turned to go home. After we had climbed back up to the bridge, I said hesitantly that I would have to head for home myself.

"You can't be in that much of a hurry," Franz laughed. "We're going in the same direction, aren't we?"

Slowly he ambled on and I didn't dare run off; he was in fact walking in the direction of my house. When we stood in front of it and I saw the front door and the big brass knocker, the sun in the windows and the curtain in my mother's room, I breathed a sigh of relief.

When I quickly opened the door and slipped in, reaching to slam it shut, Franz Kromer edged in behind me. In the cool tiled passageway, lit only by one window facing the courtyard, he stood beside me, held on to me and said softly:

"Don't be in such a rush, you."

I looked at him, terrified. His grip on my arm was like a vise. I wondered what he might have in mind and whether he wanted to hurt me. I tried to decide whether if I screamed now, screamed loud and piercingly, someone could come down from above quickly enough to save me. But I gave up the idea.

"What is it?" I asked. "What do you want?"

"Nothing much. I only wanted to ask you something. The others don't have to hear it."

"Oh, really? I can't think of anything to say to you. I have to go up, you know."

Softly Franz Kromer asked, "You know who owns the orchard by the mill, don't you?"

"I'm not sure. The miller, I think."

Franz had put his arm around me and now he drew me so close I was forced to look into his face inches away. His eyes were evil; he smiled maliciously; his face was filled with cruelty and a sense of power.

"Well, I can tell you for certain whose orchard that is. I've known for some time that someone had stolen apples there and that the man who owns it said he'd give two marks to anyone who'd tell him who swiped them."

"Oh, my God!" I exclaimed. "You wouldn't do that, would you?"

I felt it would be useless to appeal to his sense of honor. He came from the other world: betrayal was no crime to him. I sensed this acutely. The people from the other world were not like us in these matters.

"Not say anything?" laughed Kromer. "Kid, what do you take me for? Do you think I own a mint? I'm poor, I don't have a wealthy father like you, and if I can earn two marks, I earn them any way I can. Maybe he'll even give me more."

Suddenly he let go of me. The passageway no longer smelled of peace and safety, the world around me began to crumble. He would give me away to the police! I was a criminal; my father would be informed— perhaps even the police would come. All the dread of chaos threatened me; everything ugly and dangerous was united against me. It meant nothing that I'd filched nothing. I'd sworn I had!

Tears welled up in my eyes. I felt I had to strike a bargain and desperately I groped through all my pockets. Not a single apple, no pocket knife, I had nothing at all. I thought of my watch, an old silver watch that didn't work, that I wore just for the fun of it. It had been my grandmother's. Quickly I took it off.

I said, "Kromer, listen! Don't give me away. It wouldn't be fair if you did. I'll give you my watch as a present; here, take a look. Otherwise I've nothing at all. You can have it; it's made of silver, and the works— well, there's something slightly wrong with them; you have to have it fixed."

He smiled and weighed the watch in his palm. I looked at his hand and felt how brutal and deeply hostile it was to me, how it reached for my life and peace.

"It's made of silver," I said hesitantly.

"I don't give a damn for your silver and your old watch," he said scornfully. "Get it fixed yourself."

"But, Franz!" I exclaimed, trembling with fear that he might run away. "Wait, wait a moment. Why don't you take it? It's really made of silver, honest. And I don't have anything else."

He threw me a cold scornful look.

"Well, you know who I'll go to. Or I could go to the police too. . . . I'm on good terms with the sergeant."

He turned as if to go. I held on to his sleeve. I couldn't allow him to go. I would rather have died than suffer what might happen if he went off like that.

"Franz," I implored, hoarse with excitement, "don't do anything foolish. You're only joking, aren't you?"

"Yes, I'm joking, but it could turn into an expensive joke."

"Just tell me what I'm supposed to do, Franz. I'll do anything you ask."

He looked me up and down with narrowed eyes and laughed again.

"Don't be so stupid," he said with false good humor. "You know as well as I that I'm in a position to earn two marks. I'm not a rich man who can afford to throw them away, but you're rich—you even have a watch. All you have to do is give me two marks; then everything will be all right."

I understood his logic. But two marks! That was as much and as unattainable as ten, as a hundred, as a thousand. I didn't have a pfennig. There was a piggy bank that my mother kept for me. When relatives came to visit they would drop in five- or ten-pfennig pieces. That was all I had. I had no allowance at that time.

"I just don't have any," I said sadly. "I don't have any money at all. But I'll give you everything else I have. I have a Western, tin soldiers, a compass. Wait, I'll get them for you."

Kromer's mouth merely twisted into a brief sneer. Then he spit on the floor.

Harshly he said, "You can keep your crap. A compass! Don't make me mad! You hear, I'm after money."

"But I don't have any, I never get any, I can't help it."

"All right, then you'll bring me the two marks tomorrow. I'll wait for you after school down near the market place. That's all. You'll see what'll happen if you don't bring it."

"But where am I going to get it if I don't have any?"

"There's plenty of money in your house. That's your business. Tomorrow after school. And I'm telling you: if you don't have it with you . . ." He threw me a withering look, spat once more, and vanished like a shadow.

III

I couldn't even get upstairs. My life was wrecked. I thought of running away and never coming back, or of drowning myself. However, I couldn't picture any of this very clearly. In the dark, I sat down on the bottom step of our staircase, huddled up within myself, abandoning myself to misery. That's where Lina found me weeping as she came downstairs with the basket to fetch wood.

I begged her not to say a word; then I went upstairs. To the right of the glass door hung my father's hat and my mother's parasol; they gave me a feeling of home and comfort, and my heart greeted them thankfully, as the Prodigal Son might greet the sight and smell of old familiar rooms. But all of it was lost to me now; all of it belonged to the clear, well-lighted world of my father and mother, and I, guilty and deeply engulfed in an alien world, was entangled in adventures and sin, threatened by an enemy—by dangers, fear, and shame.

The hat and parasol, the old sandstone floor I was so fond of, the broad picture above the hall cupboard, the voice of my elder sister coming to me from the living room were all more moving, more precious, more delicious than ever before, but they had ceased to be a refuge and something I could rely on; they had become an unmistakable reproach. None of this was mine any more, I could no longer take part in its quiet cheerfulness. My feet had become muddied, I could not even wipe them clean on the mat; everywhere I went I was followed by a darkness of which this world of home knew nothing. How many secrets I had had, how often I had been afraid—but all of it had been child's play compared with what I brought home with me today.

I was haunted by misfortune; it was reaching out toward me so that not even my mother could protect me, since she was not even allowed to know. Whether my crime was stealing or lying (hadn't I sworn a false oath by God and everything that was sacred?) was immaterial. My sin was not specifically this or that but consisted of having shaken hands with the devil. Why had I gone along? Why had I obeyed Kromer—better

29

even than I had ever obeyed my father? Why had I invented the story, building myself up with a crime as though it were a heroic act? The devil held me in his clutches; the enemy was behind me.

For the time being I was not so much afraid of what would happen tomorrow as of the horrible certainty that my way, from now on, would lead farther and farther downhill into darkness. I felt acutely that new offenses were bound to grow out of this one offense, that my presence among my sisters, greeting and kissing my parents, were a lie, that I was living a lie concealed deep inside myself.

For a moment, hope and confidence flickered up inside me as I gazed at my father's hat. I would tell him everything, would accept his verdict and his punishment, and would make him into my confessor and savior. It would only be a penance, the kind I had often done, a bitterly difficult hour, a ruefully difficult request for forgiveness.

How sweet and tempting that sounded! But it was no use. I knew I wouldn't do it. I knew I now had a secret, a sin which I would have to expiate alone. Perhaps I stood at the parting of the ways, perhaps I would now belong among the wicked forever, share their secrets, depend on them, obey them, have to become one of their kind. I had acted the man and hero; now I had to bear the consequences.

I was glad when my father took me to task for my muddy boots. It diverted his attention by sidestepping the real issue and placed me in a position to endure reproaches that I could secretly transfer to the other, the more serious offense. A strange new feeling overcame me at this point, a feeling that stung pleasurably: I felt superior to my father! Momentarily I felt a certain loathing for his ignorance. His upbraiding me for muddy boots seemed pitiful. "If you only knew" crossed my mind as I stood there like a criminal being cross-examined for a stolen loaf of bread when the actual crime was murder.

It was an odious, hostile feeling, but it was strong and deeply attractive, and shackled me more than anything else to my secret and my guilt. I thought Kromer might have gone to the police by now and denounced me, that thunderstorms were forming above my head, while all this time they continued to treat me like a little child.

This moment was the most significant and lasting of the whole experience. It was the first rent in the holy image of my father; it was the first fissure in the columns that had upheld my childhood, which every individual must destroy before he can become himself.

Translated from the German

If you love me, I'll love you

If you hit me, I'll hit you.
If you trip me, I'll trip you.
If you kick me, I'll kick you. . . .

If you hate me, I'll hate you.
But what if I don't?

If you hug me, I'll hug you.
If you squeeze me, I'll squeeze you.
If you kiss me, I'll kiss you.
And that's one thing I can do.
If you love me, I'll love you.

From "If You Hit Me," an
acrobatic carnival dance (Cuba/Africa).

THE GOOD SAMARITAN

LUKE 10 : 25–37

And, behold, a certain lawyer stood up, and tempted him, saying, Master, what shall I do to inherit eternal life?

He said unto him, What is written in the law? how readest thou?

And he answering said, Thou shalt love the Lord thy God with all thy heart, and with all thy soul, and with all thy strength, and with all thy mind; and thy neighbor as thyself.

And he said unto him, Thou hast answered right: this do, and thou shalt live.

But he, willing to justify himself, said unto Jesus, And who is my neighbor?

And Jesus answering said, A certain man went down from Jerusalem to Jericho, and fell among thieves, which stripped him of his raiment, and wounded him, and departed, leaving him half dead.

And by chance there came down a certain priest that way; and when he saw him, he passed by on the other side.

And likewise a Levite, when he was at the place, came and looked on him, and passed by on the other side.

But a certain Samaritan, as he journeyed, came where he was; and when he saw him, he had compassion on him, and went to him, and bound up his wounds, pouring in oil and wine, and set him on his own beast, and brought him to an inn, and took care of him.

And on the morrow when he departed, he took out two pence, and gave them to the host, and said unto him, Take care of him: and whatsoever thou spendest more, when I come again, I will repay thee.

Which now of these three, thinkest thou, was neighbor unto him that fell among the thieves?

And he said, He that showed mercy on him. Then said Jesus unto him, Go, and do thou likewise.

THE FOLLY OF MOURNING

BUDDHIST PARABLE

Retold by Paul Carus

Kisā Gotamī had an only son, and he died. In her grief she carried the dead child to all her neighbors, asking them for medicine, and the people said, "She has lost her senses. The boy is dead."

At length Kisā Gotamī met a man who replied to her request, "I cannot give thee medicine for thy child, but I know a physician who can."

And the girl said: "Pray tell me, sir, who is it?" And the man replied: "Go to Sakyamuni, the Buddha."

Kisā Gotamī repaired to the Buddha and cried, "Lord and Master, give me the medicine that will cure my boy."

The Buddha answered, "I want a handful of mustard seed." And when the girl in her joy promised to procure it, the Buddha added, "The mustard seed must be taken from a house where no one has lost a child, husband, parent, or friend."

Poor Kisā Gotamī now went from house to house, and the people pitied her and said, "Here is mustard seed; take it!" But when she asked, "Did a son or daughter, a father or mother, die in your family?" they answered her, "Alas! the living are few, but the dead are many. Do not remind us of our deepest grief." And there was no house but some beloved one had died in it.

Kisā Gotamī became weary and hopeless, and sat down at the wayside, watching the lights of the city, as they flickered up and were extinguished again. At last the darkness of the night reigned everywhere. And she considered the fate of men, that their lives flicker up and are extinguished. And she thought to herself: "How selfish am I in my grief! Death is common to all; yet in this valley of desolation there is a path that leads him to immortality who has surrendered all selfishness."

Putting away the selfishness of her affection for her child, Kisā Gotamī had the dead body buried in the forest. Returning to the Buddha, she took refuge in him and found comfort in the dharma[1] which is a balm that will soothe all the pains of our troubled hearts.

The Buddha said, "The life of mortals in this world is troubled and brief and combined with pain. For there is not any means by which those that have been born can avoid dying. After reaching old age there is death; of such a nature are living beings.

"As ripe fruits are early in danger of falling, so mortals when born are always in danger of death.

"As all earthen vessels made by the potter end in being broken, so is the life of mortals.

"Both young and adult, both those who are fools and those who are wise, all fall into the power of death; all are subject to death.

"Of those who, overcome by death, depart from life, a father cannot save his son, nor kinsmen their relations.

"Mark! while relatives are looking on and lamenting deeply, one by one mortals are carried off, like an ox that is led to the slaughter.

"So the world is afflicted with death and decay; therefore the wise do not grieve, knowing the terms of the world.

"In whatever manner people think a thing will come to pass, it is often different when it happens, and great is the disappointment; see, such are the terms of the world.

"Not from weeping nor from grieving will anyone obtain peace of mind; on the contrary, his pain will be the greater and his body will suffer. He will make himself sick and pale, yet the dead are not saved by his lamentation.

"People pass away, and their fate after death will be according to their deeds.

"If a man live a hundred years, or even more, he will at last be separated from the company of his relatives, and leave the life of this world.

"He who seeks peace should draw out the arrow of lamentation, and complaint, and grief.

"He who has drawn out the arrow and has become composed will obtain peace of mind; he who has overcome all sorrow will become free from sorrow, and be blessed."

[1]*dharma:* the righteous way, virtue, truth.

Zen Stories

JAPANESE TRADITIONAL

Retold by Paul Reps

Temper

A Zen student came to Bankei and complained: "Master, I have an ungovernable temper. How can I cure it?"

"You have something very strange," replied Bankei. "Let me see what you have."

"Just now I cannot show it to you," replied the other.

"When can you show it to me?" asked Bankei.

"It arises unexpectedly," replied the student.

"Then," concluded Bankei, "it must not be your own true nature. If it were, you could show it to me at any time. When you were born you did not have it, and your parents did not give it to you. Think that over."

Cup of Tea

Nan-in, a Japanese master during the Meiji era (1868–1912), received a university professor who came to inquire about Zen.

Nan-in served tea. He poured his visitor's cup full, and then kept on pouring.

The professor watched the overflow until he no longer could restrain himself. "It is overfull. No more will go in!"

"Like this cup," Nan-in said, "you are full of your own opinions and speculations. How can I show you Zen unless you first empty your cup?"

As you sow, so shall thou reap

5.

Sir, prior to leaving I have a mind to beat you about the head and shoulders with my lead-filled shooting-stick.

7. MORAL : Never sneer at a snake on a string

SUDDENLY,

without warning.

NOKO SPRINGS

6.

and the stranger drops....

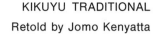

WANGOMBE

Wangombe led his regiment along the riverside until they came to a sacred grove, under which several bulls had been slaughtered and their blood collected in raw hides spread in a basin-like hole in the ground. The ceremonial place was well hidden from view by the high banks of the river and the thick forest above; only those who knew the secret passages through the giant rocks could find their way down to it. Scouts were stationed along the ridge to give warning if they saw any stranger approaching the secret entrances.

When the warriors arrived at the sacred grove, Wangombe called a halt. At his command they lined up in fours. Standing in front of them, his eyes glaring as though he were about to attack, he lifted up his long spear and raised his shield above his shoulder. Without a word he trotted rhythmically towards the warm bull's blood, and kneeling down he took a long draught of the beverage, which the war doctor was stirring with a forked twig.

In a few seconds he jumped to his feet like a disturbed lion, and with a powerful and fierce voice he burst into a song of command: "Hio-ho-o-o-o; itimo-nango-ho-o-o, na-ro-hio-hio-ho-o-o-o.

"Brave warriors, lift up your sharp spears; hio-ho-o-o-o. Fix your eyes on the foe like hungry eagles swooping upon their prey; io-ho-o-o-o.

"Vultures are floating above waiting for you to feed them: hio-ho-o-o-o.

"Is there anyone here who is afraid and trembles? Hio-ho-o-o-o. If there is, let him go home and wear his mother's skirt and front apron: hio-ho-o-o-o.

39

"Let brave warriors lift up their spears and hold shields above their shoulders: hio-ho-o-o-o.

"Let them advance and sip the warm bull's blood, vowing that they will fight to the last drop of their blood: hio-ho-o-o-o."

He concluded his recitation with a high-pitched note: "Hio-ho-o-o-o; ho-ra-re-yo-o-o-ho-o-o-o!"

The warriors, who stood erect, tossing their heads in a warlike manner, now advanced, and following their leader's example each drank. Then, shaking their plumed headgear frantically, they answered in unison:

"Hio-ho-o-o-o; ho-ra-re-yo-o-o-ho-o-o-o! We go forward to win the battle or die in the attempt: hio-ho-o-o. We will crush our enemies like a black ants' nest: hio-ho-o-o-o. Like the sting of the bee, we will thrust our sharp spears into their flesh: hio-ho-o-o-o; ho-ra-re-yo-o-o-ho-o-o-o."

When the ceremony was over, Wangombe ordered his comrades to rest and refresh themselves with meat which had been roasted on an open fire. On the ridge above, at the edge of the forest, there were several cattle kraals which the fierce Masai warriors had planned to raid. It was now about sunset; the council of war was discussing a plan for deceiving the enemy. It was decided that the cattle should be brought ostentatiously into the kraals, and that after dark they should be secretly driven away to places of safety, leaving behind only a few inferior ones whose mooing would entice the invading Masai.

Messengers were sent to the herdsmen to inform them what the Njama had decided and to instruct them to act accordingly. Spies, some disguised as Masai warriors and others as Ndorobo, had been sent into the enemy's camps, and had brought information that the Masai had decided to raid the kraals early in the morning; their scouts had informed them about the festivities which were going on in the Kikuyu country. Since the warriors were thought to be busy, the Masai warriors did not expect to meet with a strong resistance.

The spies reported that they had heard the Masai say boastfully, "The tillers of the soil love their dancing too much; they dance and dance, and then drink their dirty millet gruel in which their womenfolk have dipped their defiled hands. Then, with their bellies hanging like cala-bashes, they go to sleep like old women. What do they know about cattle? Their profession is to dig the land, and to drink polluted beverage. How can they fight with us who never let a woman touch our meat or come near us when we are feasting? E-Ngai[1] has given us the right to possess large flocks and herds. But these tillers of the soil have no right to own them. Cattle are our heritage and it is our duty to take them into our care. Tomorrow, before these slumberers recover from their dancing fatigue, we will be driving their cattle towards our sacred plains of Laikipia, for that is where they belong."

[1]*E-Ngai:* the High God. The name, Kenya, is derived from *Kere-Nyaga* the mountain of mystery, or the abode of Nyaga or Ngai, the High God.

The Kikuyu warriors listened to the report in silence, and then with fury they said to one another, "We will show these impudent thieves that we can till the land and fight as well!"

In the dead of the night, the Kikuyu warriors, marshalled by Wangombe, rose and went stealthily, their rattles covered with dried banana leaves. They hid themselves in the bush around the almost empty kraals. There they waited excitedly for the enemy. Early in the morning, when in the northeast the reflection of the rising sun brightened the sky like a polished sword and the morning stars were throwing their fading lights over the crest of mighty Kere-Nyaga, word was passed on to warn the warriors to be ready and to await the signal from the scouts.

The Masai, unaware of the preparation which the Kikuyu had made for the defence of their cattle, marched boldly towards the kraals, determined to kill anyone who came in their way, and to drive off their booty. On reaching a ford where several paths leading to various kraals met, they halted to prepare themselves for the attack.

At the command of their leader they lifted up their spears and held their shields in position. With a yell, they dashed forward like hungry leopards springing to their prey; like a gust of wind they sped over the slope and in a short time surrounded the kraals and were wildly pulling away the thorny branches blocking the entrances.

When they were thus engaged a warning horn was sounded. Like lightning the bowmen who were stationed on a little hill nearby sent a volley of poisoned arrows which fell on the Masai like a swarm of bees; the men with slings followed with a shower of stones. In a twinkling Wangombe's regiment closed with the Masai.

First the club throwers hurled their war clubs, and there was a sound of thunder as they crashed down on thick rows of upraised shields. Some struck with terrific force not on the shields but on heads, and the unfortunate Masai warriors dropped to the ground with their skulls split open. But their comrades never wavered though taken by surprise; they closed their ranks and advanced with yells of fury.

The club throwers stood upright and drew their swords, while the spearmen advanced a step forward. The warriors of both sides now came together, fighting hand to hand in a raging mass. Swords and spears in practiced hands were dancing like reeds in the water. Spearmen crouched on the ground and thrust their spears upward at their enemies' legs, ribs, and faces. Others, crippled suddenly in full charge, spun round with quivering weapons until they toppled over. Others, with arrows sticking deep in their flesh, went on thrusting and hewing until the poison overcame them and their fingers would no longer close over their sword hilts.

The Masai fought like mad dogs, but the first shower of poisoned arrows had weakened their ranks. Many of them were lying still, or squirming in a death agony, and their blood was running in streams down the hillocks and collecting in little pools on the ground.

Suddenly, finding the force against them too strong, they bolted in a great panic. Fiercely the Kikuyu warriors followed them down the slopes. When the Masai warriors reached the ford, which a short while ago they had crossed without meeting any resistance, they were met by Wamahio's regiment, which had gone to cut them off at the rear. They tried to force their way through but were overpowered.

Wangombe, who was at their heels, pressed forward, with his spear aiming at a tall warrior whose lion's mane headgear he longed to carry home as a war trophy. He was about to thrust his spear into the enemy's flesh, when suddenly he heard a beseeching cry: *"Ole yoyo, tapala,"* meaning "Brother, stop!" He could hardly believe his eyes. He was face to face with an old playmate, who as a young boy had gone to Masailand with his Kikuyu mother when she married a Masai elder.

In order to avoid annihilation of the Masai and to save his playfellow, who was at the head of the enemy's regiment, Wangombe shouted for a halt. Speaking in the Masai language, he called on the Masai warriors to surrender.

With dignity those who were left put down their weapons, and each held a handful of Nyarageta grass in his right hand as a sign of peace. Immediately a lamb was sent for, and slaughtered on the spot.

There and then a treaty of friendship was entered into. To cool down their fighting spirit, the warriors of both sides rubbed their feet with the contents of the lamb's stomach. Each promised the other not to have any more raids on their friends' territory, and that in the future if they wished to raid other territories they would act as allies. The wounded were tended; the dead were left on the battlefield to feed the hyenas and vultures, and at the same time to fertilize the soil.

From that time on the two sections remained friends. The friendship was later strengthened when a cattle disease devastated both Masai and Kikuyu cattle. The Masai, who depend entirely on the milk, meat, and blood from their cattle, experienced great hardship and thousands of them died of starvation. But the section which had established friendship with the Kikuyu were saved, for during this time trading relations were established and marketing centers were set up.

In the markets, or sometimes in the homesteads, the Kikuyu women brought grain, yams, flour, sweet potatoes, and bananas, which the Masai women bought with sheep, skins, or hides. The Masai warriors, who hitherto had regarded the cultivated crops as things cursed by the E-Ngai, now ate garden produce ravenously and comforted themselves with the excuse that *"Ciatura ngoyo ireaga ngumo,"* that is, "When there is only one article there is no choice."

FoReFATHeRS

BIRAGO DIOP

Listen more often to things rather than beings.
Hear the fire's voice,
Hear the voice of water.
In the wind hear the sobbing of the trees,
It is our forefathers breathing.

The dead are not gone forever.
They are in the paling shadows
And in the darkening shadows.
The dead are not beneath the ground,
They are in the rustling tree,
In the murmuring wood,
In the still water,
In the flowing water,
In the lonely place, in the crowd;
The dead are not dead.

Listen more often to things rather than beings.
Hear the fire's voice.
Hear the voice of water.
In the wind hear the sobbing of the trees.
It is the breathing of our forefathers
Who are not gone, not beneath the ground,
Not dead.

The dead are not gone forever.
They are in a woman's breast,
A child's crying, a glowing ember.
The dead are not beneath the earth,
They are in the flickering fire,
In the weeping plant, the groaning rock,
The wooded place, the home.
The dead are not dead.

Listen more often to things rather than beings.
Hear the fire's voice,
Hear the voice of water.
In the wind hear the sobbing of the trees.
It is the breath of our forefathers.

Translated from the French

The Brave Man of Golo

HAUSA TRADITIONAL

Retold by Harold Courlander

A man named Seidu lived in the village of Golo. Whenever the men of his village went hunting and returned with game, Seidu said to his wife, "Among all the hunters, I was the bravest. Single-handed I fought with the leopard and chased the elephant. I went forward with my spear, and the lion fled. I am the bravest of hunters."

His wife, Ladi, replied, "Did no one but you bring back meat?"

Seidu said, "Yes, because of my fearlessness, the others also had good luck."

Again, when it was said that the enemy was approaching, Seidu went into the bush country with the men, and when he returned, he hung his spear on the wall and said to his wife, "The enemy came forward; I went forward. When I ran at them, they turned and fled. My reputation has spread everywhere. I am the bravest of warriors. What is your opinion?"

Ladi answered, "It is so."

There was a funeral one time in another village, and some of the women of Golo wished to go. But the men were working in the fields and could not leave their work. Ladi told the women, "My husband is the bravest of men. He will take us through the forest."

She went to Seidu, saying, "The women who are going to the funeral agree that you are the one to take them through the forest. Will you go?"

Seidu said, "From one day to another no one mentions my courage. But when courage is needed, people ask, 'Where is Seidu?' Nevertheless, I will come."

He took his spear and went with the women through the forest.

There were warriors of the enemy in the forest. They were hunting game. When they saw Seidu coming with the women, they said, "Look how the man struts like a guinea cock. Let us strike fear into him."

They waited near the trail, and when the people of Golo came, the hunters came out of the brush before them and behind them.

Seidu shouted, "We are surrounded! Run for the trees!"

The women ran among the trees. Seidu ran with them. But there were enemy among the trees, and they seized all the people from Golo.

45

The leader of the hunters said to Seidu's wife, "What is your name?" She replied, "Ladi."

He said, "Ladi is a name used by the women of our tribe also. Because you are called Ladi, we shall not hurt you."

He said to another woman, "What is your name?"

Seeing how good it was to be named Ladi, the woman replied, "My name too is Ladi."

The leader of the hunters said, "A good name; we shall not hurt you."

He asked another woman, and she too replied, "Ladi." All of the women were asked, and all of them answered, "My name is Ladi."

Then the leader of the hunters spoke to Seidu. "All the women of your village are named Ladi. It is a strange custom. In our village each woman has a different name. But you, guinea cock who leads the guinea hens, what are you called?"

"I," Seidu said, "I too am called Ladi. My name is Ladi also."

When the hunters heard Seidu's reply, they laughed. The leader of the hunters declared, "No, it is not possible. Ladi is a woman's name. You are a man with a spear. Do not tell me that the men of your village are also called Ladi?"

Seidu said, "No, no, only the women are called Ladi."

The hunters said, "How then are you called Ladi?"

Seidu looked one way and another way, but he saw no chance of escape. He said, "You see, appearances are deceiving. I also am a woman."

The enemy laughed. They could not stop laughing. The women of Golo laughed too.

Seidu's wife spoke. She said, "He speaks badly of himself. He is the courageous Seidu, the famous Seidu."

Seidu said then, "Yes, it is so."

A hunter said, "People say that Seidu claims to be the bravest of all men."

"No," Seidu replied, "it is no longer so. *Formerly* I was the bravest of all men. Today it is different. From now on I shall be only the bravest in my village."

The hunters let them go. Seidu and the women went to the funeral, and they returned afterward to their own houses. When they arrived in Golo, everyone was laughing at Seidu. Instead of calling him by his name, they called him Ladi. He went into his house and closed the door. Whenever he came out, they laughed. He could not hide from the shame.

At last he sent his wife to tell them this, "Seidu who was formerly the bravest of men was reduced to being the bravest in his village. But from now on he is not the bravest in the village. He agrees to be only as brave as other people."

So the people of Golo stopped ridiculing Seidu. And thereafter he was no braver than anyone else.

A Worker Reads History

BERTOLT BRECHT

Who built the seven gates of Thebes?
The books are filled with names of kings.
Was it kings who hauled the craggy blocks of stone?
And Babylon, so many times destroyed,
Who built the city up each time? In which of Lima's houses,
That city glittering with gold, lived those who built it?
In the evening when the Chinese wall was finished
Where did the masons go? Imperial Rome
Is full of arcs of triumph. Who reared them up? Over whom
Did the Caesars triumph? Byzantium lives in song,
Were all her dwellings palaces? And even in Atlantis of the legend
The night the sea rushed in,
The drowning men still bellowed for their slaves.

Young Alexander conquered India.
He alone?
Caesar beat the Gauls.
Was there not even a cook in his army?
Philip of Spain wept as his fleet
Was sunk and destroyed. Were there no other tears?
Frederick the Great triumphed in the Seven Years War. Who
Triumphed with him?

Each page a victory,
At whose expense the victory ball?
Every ten years a great man,
Who paid the piper?

So many particulars.
So many questions.

Translated by H. R. Hays

from **ZORBA**

THE GREEK

NIKOS KAZANTZAKIS

On one of these Sundays, as we were returning from the copious feast, I decided to speak and tell Zorba of my plans. He listened, gaping and forcing himself to be patient. But from time to time he shook his great head with anger. When I had finished, he nervously plucked two or three hairs from his mustache.

"I hope you don't mind my saying so, boss, but I don't think your brain is quite formed yet. How old are you?"

"Thirty-five."

"Then it never will be."

Thereupon he burst out laughing. I was stung to the quick.

"You don't believe in man, do you?" I retorted.

"Now, don't get angry, boss. No, I don't believe in anything. If I believed in man, I'd believe in God, and I'd believe in the devil, too. And that's a whole business. Things get all muddled then, boss, and cause me a lot of complications."

He became silent, took off his beret, scratched his head frantically, and tugged again at his mustache, as if he meant to tear it off. He wanted to say something, but he restrained himself. He looked at me out of the corner of his eye; looked at me again and decided to speak.

"Man is a brute," he said, striking the pebbles with his stick. "A great brute. Your lordship doesn't realize this. It seems everything's been too easy for you, but you ask me! A brute, I tell you! If you're cruel to him, he respects and fears you. If you're kind to him, he plucks your eyes out.

"Keep your distance, boss! Don't make men too bold; don't go telling them we're all equal, we've got the same rights, or they'll go straight and trample on *your* rights; they'll steal your bread and leave you to die of hunger. Keep your distance, boss, by all the good things I wish you!"

"But don't you believe in anything?" I exclaimed in exasperation.

"No, I don't believe in anything. How many times must I tell you that? I don't believe in anything or anyone; only in Zorba. Not because Zorba is better than the others; not at all, not a little bit! He's a brute like the rest! But I believe in Zorba because he's the only being I have in my power, the only one I know. All the rest are ghosts. I see with these eyes, I hear with these ears, I digest with these guts. All the rest are ghosts, I tell you. When I die, everything'll die. The whole Zorbatic world will go to the bottom!"

"What egoism!" I said sarcastically.

"I can't help it, boss! That's how it is. I eat beans, I talk beans; I am Zorba, I talk like Zorba."

I said nothing. Zorba's words stung me like whiplashes. I admired him for being so strong, for despising men to that extent, and at the same time wanting to live and work with them. I should either have become an ascetic or else have adorned men with false feathers so that I could put up with them.

Zorba looked round at me. By the light of the stars I could see he was grinning from ear to ear.

"Have I offended you, boss?" he said, stopping abruptly. We had arrived at the hut. Zorba looked at me tenderly and uneasily.

I did not reply. I felt my mind was in agreement with Zorba, but my heart resisted, wanted to leap out and escape from the brute, to go its own road.

"I'm not sleepy this evening, Zorba," I said. "You go to bed."

The stars were shining, the sea was sighing and licking the shells, a glowworm lit under its belly its little lantern. Night's hair was streaming with dew.

I lay face downward, plunged in silence, thinking of nothing. I was now one with night and the sea; my mind was like a glowworm that had lit its little lantern and settled on the damp, dark earth, and was waiting.

The stars were traveling round, the hours were passing—and, when I arose, I had, without knowing how, engraved on my mind the double task I had to accomplish on this shore:

Escape from Buddha, rid myself by words of all my metaphysical cares and free my mind from vain anxiety;

Make direct and firm contact with men, starting from this very moment.

I said to myself, "Perhaps it is not yet too late."

Translated by Carl Wildman

That's what I Learned in school

What did you learn in school today
dear little boy of mine?
What did you learn in school today
dear little boy of mine?
I learned that Washington
never told a lie
I learned that soldiers seldom die
I learned that everybody's free
That's what the teacher said to me
And that's what I learned in school today
That's what I learned in school

From "What Did You Learn in School Today?"
words and music by Tom Paxton (U.S.A.)

LIES

YEVGENY YEVTUSHENKO

Telling lies to the young is wrong.
Proving to them that lies are true is wrong.
Telling them that God's in his heaven
and all's well with the world is wrong.
The young know what you mean. The young are people.
Tell them the difficulties can't be counted,
and let them see not only what will be
but see with clarity these present times.
Say obstacles exist they must encounter,
sorrow happens, hardship happens.
The hell with it. Who never knew
the price of happiness will not be happy.
Forgive no error you recognize,
it will repeat itself, increase,
and afterward our pupils
will not forgive in us what we forgave.

Translated by Peter Levi and Robin Milner–Gulland

from

To Sir with Love

E. R. BRAITHWAITE

I

I arrived early for class my first day as a teacher at the Greenslade School. As I entered the narrow alleyway leading to the school I could hear the strident voices of the early children in the playground; one girlish voice was raised in violent protest.

"Denham, why don't you let the bloody netball alone?"

Shocked, I walked into the forecourt, which was used as a playground, and saw a group of girls spaced around a netball standard; one of them held a netball behind her back, away from a big, loutish fellow who had interposed himself between her and the net into which she wanted to throw it.

"Move out the bloody way, youse, or I'll . . ."

At this point they heard my approach and looked around, but seeing me made little difference for, as I mounted the stairs, I could hear their voices again, brutally frank in Anglo-Saxon references. Confidence began to ooze out of me; would they actually use words like that in the classroom? The idea was fantastic.

Mrs. Drew was sitting in the staffroom reading her newspaper. I greeted her and removed my overcoat.

"All set for the fray?" Her voice was soft, sympathetic.

"I think so. Mrs. Drew, do the children use bad language inside the school, in the classrooms?"

"Sometimes." There was always a gravity behind her remarks, indicative of a really deep concern for the children, and a certain objective examination of her own efforts on their behalf. "Most of the time they are merely showing off. The words themselves are not in their minds associated with the acts they suggest, and it is often good policy to behave as if one did not hear. Some of the older ones deliberately set out to shock, to offend. I get very little of it these days—I suppose out of deference to my gray hairs." She patted her neat coiffure. "I'm afraid I cannot tell you how to deal with it; you'll just have to do the best you can."

One by one the staff arrived and soon there was a pleasing interchange of chatter until the morning bell rang.

As I was leaving the room I looked across at Miss Blanchard and she smiled her encouragement. Miss Clintridge called out cheerily, "Good luck."

From outside the classroom I could hear sounds of talk, laughter, and movement. I went in and walked directly to my desk, seated myself and waited. The children were standing about in groups and had paid no attention to my entrance; but gradually, the groups dispersed and they seated themselves. I waited until everyone was quietly settled, then called the attendance register.

Their replies to their names were mostly mumbles or grunts, with here or there a "yep" or "here." One boy answered "Here, Sir," and this promptly provoked a chorus of jeers from boys and girls alike.

Registration over, I sat back to take my first careful look at the class before we were summoned into the auditorium for daily assembly. A quick count revealed forty-six positions, forty-two of which were occupied. They were set in four straight lines and from my desk I commanded a clear view of them all. Twenty-six of the class were girls, and many of their faces bore traces of make-up inexpertly or hurriedly removed, giving to their obvious youth a slightly tawdry, jaded look. . . .

The boys were scruffier, coarser, dirtier; everything about them indicated a planned conformity—the T-shirts, jeans, haircuts, the same wary sullenness. None of it really belonged to them. It was worn, assumed in and out of school like a kind of armor, a gesture against authority, a symbol of toughness as thin and synthetic as the cheap films from which it was copied.

I said, "The Headmaster has told you my name, but it will be some little while before I know all yours, so in the meantime I hope you won't mind if I point at you or anything like that; it will not be meant rudely." I tried to inject as much pleasant informality as possible into my voice. "I do not know anything about you or your abilities, so I will begin from scratch. One by one I'll listen to you reading; when I call your name will you please read anything you like from any one of your schoolbooks."

I sat down, opened the attendance register and called one name at random. "Palmer, will you read for us, please."

I followed the gaze of the class and discovered that Palmer was a red-faced, bullnecked boy, with pale eyes and a very large close-cropped head.

"Will you stand up, please?"

He looked around the class indecisively, then rose to his feet and began to read slowly, haltingly.

"That will do, Palmer. Now, Benjamin, will you carry on?"

Palmer sat down, looking at me questioningly. His reading was shockingly bad. Benjamin's effort was not much better, nor was that of Sapiano, Wells, or Drake.

"Potter, will you read, please?"

Potter was tall and very fat, easily the largest boy in the class. He read reasonably well, and when I raised my hand for him to stop, he beamed happily.

"Sit down, Potter." My voice was sharp. "I take it you would all agree that this book is written in English, your language and that of your ancestors. After listening to you, I am not sure whether you are reading badly deliberately, or are unable to understand or express your own language. However, it may be that I have done you the injustice of selecting the worst readers. Would anyone else like to read for me?"

There was a pause, then a hand shot up at the farthest end of the back row. It belonged to the redhead whom I had encountered the day before. I noticed that unlike most of the class she was clean and neat.

"Your name, please?"

"Dare, Pamela Dare."

"Begin, please."

Her voice was clear, warm, and well-modulated; she read easily, flowing the words into a clear picture of the boy's terrifying experience. The passage ended, she stopped and looked at me defiantly, as if satisfied with this vindication of her colleagues, then abruptly sat down.

"Thank you, Pamela Dare. Anyone else like to try?"

No one offered, so I spoke to them at some length about reading, emphasizing that it was the most important of the basic skills they were expected to master. Occasionally I walked over to a desk at random, picked up a book, and read from it to illustrate some point I was making. They sat watching me, quietly, ominously, but they were listening, and I warmed to my subject, primarily concerned with keeping them that way. The bell for recess was a very welcome sound, and they trooped out to their midmorning milk while I sat down at my desk to give some further thought to the next lesson.

II

Before the class returned I set up the blackboard on its easel and waited for them somewhat impatiently. As soon as they were settled once more I began.

"Our arithmetic lesson will be on weights and measures. As with our reading lesson, I am again trying to find out how much you know about it and you can help by answering my questions as fully as you are able. Does anyone know the table of weights, avoirdupois?"

"Aver er what?"

"Avoirdupois," I repeated, hoping my pronunciation of the word was correct. "It refers to those weights commonly used in grocers' shops and the like."

"Yeah, I know." The thickset fellow was slumped low in his chair. "Like heavyweight, light-heavy, cruiserweight, middle, light bantam, flyweight, featherweight."

He held up both hands like a toddler in kindergarten and was playfully counting off on his fingers. When he stopped they laughed, and at that he stood up and bowed to them with mock gravity. It was really very funny, and in another place, at another time, I too would have laughed as uproariously as the rest. But, for good or ill, this was my classroom. I let the laughter run its course. I folded my arms across my chest and leaned against my desk until every last one of them had laughed his fill and subsided.

Then, "What's your name, please?" I was angry and my voice was brittle.

"Denham."

"Well, Denham, that's one way of applying the table of weights. Are you interested in boxing, Denham?"

"Yeah." He flexed his shoulders and gazed lazily around the room.

"I see. Well, if you have at least learned to apply the table in that limited respect, it cannot be said that you are altogether stupid, can it, Denham?"

The smile left his face.

"Is there anyone else who would like to say something about the table of weights?"

"Tons, hundredweights, quarters, pounds, ounces." The voice came suddenly from just in front of me.

"Yes, that's correct. What's your name, please?"

"Tich, Tich Jackson."

I felt rather pleased at this gesture of cooperation.

"In some places, like the U.S.A. and the West Indies, although they use the same table of weights, they refer to pounds or tons, but never to stones or hundredweights. So a man would speak of his weight as 170 pounds, while here in England it would be 12 stone, 2 pounds, which would put him in the cruiserweight class, I suppose."

"Welterweight." Denham's tone was casual but authoritative.

"Thank you, Denham, welterweight. There are other weights in use. Troy weight is used by jewelers in weighing precious metals like gold, silver, or platinum."

"Diamonds are a girl's best friend."

A loud roar of laughter followed this remark. I was not sure who was responsible, but I knew it came from the back row. I looked at Denham but he returned my gaze levelly, even insolently.

"Don't care for them much meself."

A stout, sallow-skinned girl removed the necklace of colored glass beads from her rather grimy neck with an elaborate gesture and held them up for general inspection.

"Pearls is more in my line."

Her mimicry and exaggerated gestures held the class helpless with laughter.

I knew that I had to do something, anything, and quickly. They were challenging my authority, probably with no feeling of antipathy to myself, but merely to maintain a kind of established convention of resistance to a new teacher, watching closely for any sign of weakness or indecision. OK, if a fight was what they wanted . . .

"That's enough!" My voice was sharp and loud, cutting off their laughter. "I find it both interesting and encouraging to discover that you have a sense of humor, especially about something as simple and elementary as weights. As a matter of fact, you seem to find everything rather amusing. You were amused at your inability to read simple passages in your own language, and now you are amused at your ignorance of weights. Many folk I have met have been disturbed, even distressed at their lack of knowledge; in your case you find such a lack amusing." I was being sarcastic, deliberately, incisively sarcastic. "It is therefore very clear to me that we shall have a most delightful time together; you seem to know so very little, and you are so easily amused, that I can look forward to a very happy time."

There were murmurs of "bleeding cheek" from some of them. They were not smiling now, but glaring angrily at me. This was much better.

"Now we'll turn our attention to measurements, beginning with linear measurement. Do you know the table of linear measurement, Denham?"

"Don't know what you mean."

"Well, before I explain I'll wait until you've all had the usual laugh."

They remained grave, angry, watchful.

"Does anyone else know the table I'm referring to?"

"Inches, feet, yards, furlongs, miles." It was the fat, freckled girl who spoke.

"Yes, that's quite correct. It's called linear because it is concerned with lines."

I then began to give them some background history on measurement and the way in which it affected the daily lives of all of us. They listened and I kept them listening until the dinner bell rang.

from

THE
400
BLOWS

FRANÇOIS TRUFFAUT

TITLE SEQUENCE. The title sequence consists of a number of traveling shots of the Eiffel Tower, taken from different angles and streets. A variety of Parisian architecture appears in the foreground. The theme music continues throughout the sequence. (158 seconds)

1   *Close-up (CU) of a schoolroom desk, seen from over the shoulder of a young boy. He is writing. He puts down his pen and pulls a pinup picture of a girl in a bathing suit out of the desk.*

After a quick look he passes it ahead, and the picture moves rapidly up one row and across three. As the camera pans we see the class: a group of perhaps forty boys, twelve or thirteen years old, anxiously keeping up the appearance of studying for their teacher, who sits at a large desk in front. He is known to the students as LITTLE QUIZ. *The pinup makes its way to* ANTOINE DOINEL, *a dark-haired boy in a turtleneck sweater. He draws a mustache on the picture.*

LITTLE QUIZ. Doinel! Bring me what you have there.

(ANTOINE *reluctantly walks up to the teacher, a dour-looking man in a full-length coat, and hands him the picture.*)

LITTLE QUIZ. Ah! Very nice! Go stand in the corner!

(ANTOINE *goes to the corner and disappears behind a small blackboard which stands on an easel. He reappears momentarily on the other side of the easel, holding his nose and grimacing. The class laughs.*)

LITTLE QUIZ. Quiet! Only a minute left!
CLASS. Oh!
LITTLE QUIZ. Quiet! (*He moves between the rows of students.*)   (56)

2   *Medium shot (MS). The teacher walks to the back of the classroom. The students are bent over their papers in deep concentration—except for* RENÉ BIGEY, *who stares at the ceiling looking for inspiration.*

LITTLE QUIZ. The papers will be collected in thirty seconds.

(*Protests from the class.*)

LITTLE QUIZ. Quiet! (*He walks to the front of the room, stopping to encourage a tousle-headed boy by cuffing him on the head.*)
LITTLE QUIZ (*looking at his watch*). Monitors get ready. I'll count to three. One . . . two . . . three . . . Collect the papers!

(*Student monitors spring to their feet.* RENÉ *gets a sudden inspiration and begins writing; the others lift their heads and slap down their pens.*)   (34)

3 *Medium close-up (MCU).* RENÉ *is writing furiously.* BERTRAND MAURICET *tries to collect his paper, but* RENÉ *pushes him away.*

RENÉ. Collect the papers in the back!
LITTLE QUIZ *(off-screen).* What's going on?
MAURICET. He won't give me his paper, sir.
LITTLE QUIZ *(off-screen).* No favoritism.

   (MAURICET *finally pulls the paper away.*)   (16)

4 *MCU. The teacher stands in front of the easel, collecting papers.*

LITTLE QUIZ. Has everyone handed in his paper? You can go.

   (*There is a general rush to the door.* ANTOINE *pops out from behind the easel.*)

LITTLE QUIZ *(off).* Oh, no, not you, my dear student.

   (ANTOINE *stops in his tracks.* LITTLE QUIZ *walks past him, pointing toward the corner.*)

LITTLE QUIZ. Recess isn't a right. It's a reward! (*He continues to the door, his arm pointing toward the corner. He goes out and locks the door behind him.* ANTOINE *goes back to his corner, furious. As he passes the blackboard he throws an eraser in the air, but it is attached to the board by a string.*)   (32)

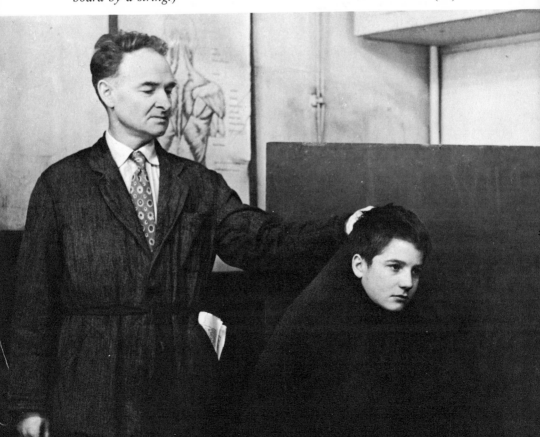

5 *Long shot (LS) from above of the schoolyard. Some students are playing games; others are involved in discussions. Two boys fight a duel with their notebooks. Another rides on his friend's back.* *(4)*

6 *MS from above. A group of students stand talking near* LITTLE QUIZ *and a colleague.* *(1)*

7 *MS from above of a group of six students. Two wrestle while another plays with a shovel. The camera pans left to several other boys who are in a pushing and shoving fight.* *(12)*

8 *CU.* ANTOINE, *in his corner, reaches up and starts writing on the wall. We hear him reading to himself.*

ANTOINE. Here suffers poor Antoine Doinel
       Unjustly punished by Little Quiz
       For a pinup that fell from heaven . . .
       Between us it'll be an eye for an eye, a
       tooth for a tooth. *(4)*

9 *MS from above. In the schoolyard,* LITTLE QUIZ *breaks up a scuffle between two boys; he grabs them by their necks and drives them out into the center of the yard.*

LITTLE QUIZ. OK, champions. What you need is a referee. You'll train for three days without a recess . . . three days of rest, that'll do you some good. Go on, go on! *(13)*

10 *CU.* ANTOINE *lowers his hand and examines his work.* *(1)*

11 *MS. The students rush back into the room.* RENÉ *breaks away from the group and runs behind the easel.* MAURICET *follows him, then sticks his head back out.*

MAURICET. Look at this!

(ANTOINE *pushes* MAURICET *away, but the damage is done. Boys crowd in on both sides of the easel.*)

LITTLE QUIZ (*off*). What's so interesting there?

(*The students flee in all directions as* LITTLE QUIZ *goes behind the easel. He pulls* ANTOINE *out by the scruff of his neck and pushes him into the room.* LITTLE QUIZ *digs his hands into his pockets in disgust.* ANTOINE *hangs his head.*) *(27)*

12 *CU.* LITTLE QUIZ *looks back and forth from* ANTOINE *to the class.*

LITTLE QUIZ (*with heavy irony*). Marvelous, we have a new Juvenal in the class! Only he can't tell the difference between an alexandrine and blank verse. *(6)*

13   *CU of* ANTOINE, *from the teacher's point of view.*

LITTLE QUIZ. First: Doinel, you will conjugate for tomorrow. . . .   *(2)*

14   *CU.* LITTLE QUIZ *stands in front of the blackboard.*

LITTLE QUIZ (*to* ANTOINE). Go to your seat.   *(2)*

15   *CU. Hanging his head,* ANTOINE *walks to his place.*

LITTLE QUIZ (*off*). Take this down. In all the tenses of the indicative, the conditional, and the subjunctive. . . .   *(6)*

16   *CU of* LITTLE QUIZ, *hands on hips.*

LITTLE QUIZ (*to the class*). The rest of you, take out your recitation note-books. (*He sits at his desk, purses his lips, and looks up at* ANTOINE.)
   (4)

17   *LS.* ANTOINE *sits down and gets ready to write.*

LITTLE QUIZ (*off*). "I deface the classroom walls, and I mistreat French prosody."   *(11)*

18   *CU.* LITTLE QUIZ *stands and goes to the blackboard.*

LITTLE QUIZ (*to the class*). "The Hare."   *(7)*

19   *MS of the class. In unison, heads drop and pens are taken up for the dictation.*   *(5)*

20   *CU. The teacher turns around with a show of weary contempt.*

LITTLE QUIZ. Second: Doinel, go immediately to the concierge and bring me something to erase this nonsense. . . .   *(3)*

21   *CU.* ANTOINE *looks up.*   *(3)*

22   *CU. The teacher. He gives a vindictive toss of his head.*

LITTLE QUIZ. Or else, my friend, I'll make you lick them off! (*The matter closed, he turns back to the board and begins writing out "The Hare." He speaks without stopping or turning around.*) Richer, who gave you permission to change places?   *(11)*

23   *CU.* ANTOINE *slaps his pen down, gets up, and walks out, dejected. The camera pans to the tousle-headed boy on the right-hand side of the room.* LITTLE QUIZ *can be heard reading the lines of "The Hare" aloud as he writes them down, his voice rising and falling. The boy writes laboriously, his head bent down and bobbing as he moves his pen across the page. Suddenly dissatisfied, he rips the page out and with some difficulty turns toward the back of his notebook.*

LITTLE QUIZ (*off*). "In the season when the
        bushes . . .
        Flame with vermilion flowers . . ." (*25*)

24 *CU. LITTLE QUIZ is writing on the board, his back to the camera.*

LITTLE QUIZ. "When the black tips . . ." (*5*)

25 *CU. The tousle-headed boy dips his pen in the inkpot, only to have the ink drip on the page. He sticks his tongue out in dismay and pulls more pages out of his notebook.* (*8*)

26 *CU. LITTLE QUIZ is writing and reciting.*

LITTLE QUIZ. ". . . of my long ears . . ." (*3*)

27 *CU. The boy starts to turn the page, but his hands are by now so ink-stained that he has to tear out more pages.*

LITTLE QUIZ (*off*). ". . . could already be seen . . . above . . ." (*11*)

28 *CU. LITTLE QUIZ looks rapidly from side to side as if he were searching for inspiration.*

LITTLE QUIZ. ". . . the still-green rye . . ." (*He turns around and looks at the class to see who's working, then whips back to the board.*) (*8*)

29 *CU. The boy is still wrestling with his notebook.*

LITTLE QUIZ (*off*). ". . . from which I nibble . . ." (*4*)

30 *CU. LITTLE QUIZ turns around in the middle of a phrase.*

LITTLE QUIZ. ". . . the tender stalks . . . as I play about . . ."   *(16)*

31   *CU. The boy accidentally drips still more ink on the pages. He desperately tears off the dirty pages and stuffs them under the desk.*

LITTLE QUIZ (*off*). "One day . . . comma . . . tired out . . ."

(*The boy lifts the notebook off the desk and is astonished at how thin it is. The camera tilts up and pans to the door as* ANTOINE *enters carrying a pan and sponge.*)

LITTLE QUIZ (*off*). "I was asleep . . . in my hutch."   *(25)*

32   *LS. The classroom from the rear.* ANTOINE *walks down the right side, waves to the class, and darts up behind the teacher to make the sign of donkey's ears behind his head.*
      Great suppressed amusement. He darts away and goes behind the easel.

LITTLE QUIZ. "Little Margot surprised me there." (LITTLE QUIZ *turns around too late to see* ANTOINE.)
LITTLE QUIZ. "I'm not the only one," eh Simonot?
SIMONOT (*popping up from his seat in the rear*). I didn't do anything, sir.
LITTLE QUIZ. Of course not. It's always someone else.   *(12)*

33   *CU.* ANTOINE *is standing in front of the wall on which he has composed his poem. He begins scrubbing.*

LITTLE QUIZ (*off*). "Indeed, she liked me. . . ."   *(3)*

34   *LS of the classroom, as in shot 32.* ANTOINE *can occasionally be seen scrubbing the corner wall behind the easel.*

LITTLE QUIZ. ". . . my affectionate little mistress."

(*At this line, some of the boys embrace each other in mock passion; others encircle their own necks to give the appearance of a couple embracing; another throws kisses to an imaginary audience of admirers.* LITTLE QUIZ *turns around and restores order with a piercing glance. He moves to his desk.*)

LITTLE QUIZ (*still reciting*).
"How good she was,
What care, what tenderness!
How she hugged me on her little knees . . ."

(*He turns to the board and the general disorder resumes, accompanied by cooing noises.*)

LITTLE QUIZ. ". . . and kissed me."

(*Whistles and sighs.* LITTLE QUIZ *swings around.*)

LITTLE QUIZ. What imbecile whistled? (*Dead silence.*) I warn you, I will be unfair—if the guilty one doesn't confess, I'll punish one of you as an example. Right, Simonot?

SIMONOT (*popping up*). I swear it wasn't me, sir.

(LITTLE QUIZ *throws the chalk at him.*)

LITTLE QUIZ. Cowards too, eh? What a year! What a class!　　　(*43*)

35　*CU of* LITTLE QUIZ, *hands on hips.*

LITTLE QUIZ. I've known idiots before, but at least they were polite. They stayed in their seats—in their corners.　　　(*4*)

36　*CU.* ANTOINE, *too frightened to return to his seat, lowers his eyes during the last part of this tirade.*

LITTLE QUIZ (*off*). And you?

(ANTOINE'S *head snaps up.*)　　　(*4*)

37　*CU.* LITTLE QUIZ *faces* ANTOINE.

LITTLE QUIZ. Do you think you've cleaned it up? No, you've made it dirtier, my friend. Go to your seat and copy this recitation.　　(*4*)

38　*CU.* ANTOINE *walks off glumly.*　　　(*1*)

39　*LS. The entire room from the back.* ANTOINE *walks to his place on the left.*

LITTLE QUIZ. I pity France in ten years! (*He goes to his desk and throws a book on the floor.*)　　　(*5*)

40　*MS. The camera tilts down from the "Liberty—Equality—Fraternity" bas-relief statuary group above the school entrance to the students pouring out of the door.* RENÉ *and* ANTOINE *come out and turn left.*

RENÉ. Everyone swipes money from his parents.
ANTOINE. Yes, but it's still difficult.
RENÉ. Even Mauricet, I bet. Hey, Mauricet . . . !

(*They stop in front of* MAURICET, *who is wearing black rubber goggles.*)

RENÉ. Where'd you buy those fancy goggles?
MAURICET. At the Hotel de Ville.
RENÉ. With dough swiped from your old man?

(MAURICET *shrugs his shoulders and walks off. They shout after him.*)

70

RENÉ. Don't tell us you didn't, you hypocrite!

ANTOINE. It was you who squealed on me!

(*They turn away and walk back past the school entrance.*)

ANTOINE (*looking back and shouting over his shoulder*). Dirty rotten stinker!

RENÉ. Your days are numbered, Mauricet!

ANTOINE. You'll get yours, Mauricet!   (*34*)

41   *LS. The two turn right onto the* Rue des Martyrs.

ANTOINE. I'll never finish tonight.

(*They approach an empty bench.*)   (*14*)

42   *CU. They sit down.*

ANTOINE. That rat Little Quiz.

RENÉ (*laughing*). That's his job.

ANTOINE. Before the Army gets us I'm going to sock him one.

(*They get up.* ANTOINE *passes behind the bench, reaches across it
to shake* RENÉ's *hand, and runs into his house.
Dissolve.*)   (*14*)

Translated by David Denby

THE DUNCE

JACQUES PRÉVERT

He says no with his head
but he says yes with his heart
he says yes to what he loves
he says no to the teacher
he stands
he is questioned
and all the problems are posed
sudden laughter seizes him
and he erases all
the words and figures
names and dates
sentences and snares
and despite the teacher's threats
to the jeers of infant prodigies
with chalk of every color
on the blackboard of misfortune
he draws the face of happiness.

Translated by Lawrence Ferlinghetti

JAN MYRDAL

Han Ying-lin, head-master, aged 28

I am the head of Liu Ling Basic School. I was born in 1934 in Lochuan. My mother is dead and my father is a farmer. He can neither read nor write. I went to school in Lochuan. By the time I was ten, I had been through the first section of the basic school, and I then went to Lochuan Normal School. In 1949, I joined the League of Youth. In 1953, I joined the party. That same year I began as a teacher. In 1958, I began as assistant to the head in Yenan Middle School. In 1960, I studied at Yenan University. In 1961, I was appointed headmaster of Liu Ling Basic School.

I was fourteen when Hu Tsung-nan's troops withdrew from the area. All my conscious life has been spent in the new society. I am a rural intellectual of the new type.

73

The school has ten teachers, one of whom is an assistant teacher who works in the whole of our district, helping schoolteachers with their own education. Most of the teachers are new. Our experience is short. The most experienced of us has ten years' service. Three of the teachers are women. We all belong to the trade union.

The school is, of course, mixed; 109 of our pupils are boys and 68 girls. We have six classes. The first four classes constitute the lower basic school and the two highest the higher basic school. The school was started in 1940 with twenty-four pupils. It closed down during the occupation, but reopened in 1949 with eight pupils. The higher basic school was opened in 1956. Our pupils come from this and surrounding labor brigades, and also from Seven-mile Village.

Our school fulfills the task the party has given us. Teaching has to serve the policy of the proletariat, and teaching has to be combined with productive work. We are to inculcate the fundamentals of knowledge and basic techniques. The pupils study, but after lessons they have to contribute, as well as they can, in productive work in the school's vegetable garden. They have to know the honor of working, so that they don't look down on work.

There are many good little workers among our pupils. I myself can remember that in my schooldays the pupils never cleaned out the latrines. If we met a farmworker carrying a couple of buckets of human excrement, we felt unclean and hid. But now, in our school, the pupils have such a feeling for the honor of work that they will crawl down into the latrines with enthusiasm and bring up the excrement. This teaches them cleanliness and respect for work.

At the parents' meetings people often say that, before, their children had not helped in the house, but that now they sweep the yard, carry the rubbish away, and collect grass for the pig. But it is not just a question of production. It is also a matter of proletarian policy. Of knowing how. The teachers are young and enthusiastic and they work hard and prepare their lessons well. Before, the teachers never bothered about anything. Now they all study so much that I have to go round at night and myself see that they put their lights out and go to sleep.

The pupils have two kinds of preparatory work: that which they do in school during private study hours and proper homework. We have rather a problem with the latter. It is often difficult for the pupils to study undisturbed at home in their caves. We have discussed this with the parents at the parents' meetings. The teachers are, besides, in touch with parents over various questions. If any problems arise with pupils, if their work is not satisfactory, or if there are difficulties at home, we discuss this at the parents' meetings and in the school management. Teachers will also go to a home and have a talk with a pupil's parents. They discuss how the pupil concerned is studying, how he lives, how he works at home.

They assess his good and his bad sides. We try to foster his good side and correct his bad side. It may also happen that parents do not consider that their children should go to school. Perhaps the family is badly off for labor and wants to have the child at home in order to put him to work. We then have a talk with the parents about the necessity for education. We try to get them to understand this and to agree.

We had one of these problems some time ago. Tuan Fu-yin, whose son Tuan Shao-tang is one of the best pupils in the school, forbade him to go to school. This was during the spring term 1962. Tuan Fu-yin wanted to have his son at home so that he could work and earn money. It took three visits before we could get this father to agree to his son's staying on at school.

All forms of physical punishment are forbidden. For a teacher to raise his hand against a pupil is a crime, no matter what the circumstances under which it is done. We discuss problems with the pupils; we discuss them with the parents. In extreme cases we can expel a pupil. But that is only on paper. We have never had to expel anyone. We have never come up against a case as grave as that. We also have different kinds of activities outside school hours. We organize the children's play because children ought to learn as they play. Then we have the work in the vegetable garden I mentioned.

The methods we use are different from those of the old days. We have no learning off by heart. We try to stimulate the pupils' own interest in what is being studied. They must want to learn the thing. School education must be such that they of their own accord long to go to school and love their studies and understand why education is necessary. The new school must be attractive. Especially now, when education is still not compulsory, and it will certainly be some time before that can be introduced.

Before, school used to train bookworms who had no understanding of real life. One of my classmates had a father who was a farmer, too. When this father came to visit his son at his school in Lochuan, the boy used to run away and hide, because he was ashamed before the others of having a father who worked with his hands. Now, pupils are brought up to do work with their own hands and to love their parents and have respect for all who are elderly. Children no longer learn mere theory, but practice as well. In mathematics, for example, we teach them to work with an abacus. One of our pupils from Seven-mile Village is already doing all the family's bookkeeping.

Because we explain to the children that the purpose of their studying is to make them fit to build up their country, our pupils now work with great enthusiasm. That was not the case in the old days. Then, one just learned things by heart. In general, the children do obey us. Their grades are not particularly good, but they themselves are good.

We attach great weight to their moral education. We hold up various models and heroes as moral examples for them. We tell them what they should do and what they should not do. We make it clear to them where the line runs between right and wrong. If something seems not clear or doubtful to them, we announce a class discussion, and, when this has been held, the teacher draws the conclusions from it for them, emphasizing right and wrong.

We instruct the children in hygiene and cleanliness. They do not know much about this when they first come to school. This is, of course, a backward, dirty part of the country. People here do not have good habits in hygiene. After our training, the children become better. We help their families to change their habits. We teach the children gradually to per-suade their parents to change their habits, where hygiene is concerned. We certainly do not encourage them to argue stubbornly with their parents. On the contrary, we attach great importance to their respecting their elders. Our task is to collaborate with their parents. School and home must stand united. Our aim is to turn the children into healthy bearers of culture, willing to work with others and loving their socialist country.

We do not want any smooth, slippery personalities. But it is very necessary that they should have the feeling of being ready to work and be collective-minded. Children ought to be group-conscious. We teach the children to help each other. Not to compete with each other, but to help each other. Take, for example, the river-crossing down here. After rain it is not easy, and so the older children have to help the younger, and the boys the girls. The older ones carry the young ones across. We also train them to be honest. If they find anything on the road, they are to bring it to school.

Our timetable follows that generally laid down for schools. In the lower basic school the lessons are of forty minutes and the breaks of fifteen. The school day begins at 8 o'clock and goes on till 12 o'clock. Afternoon work starts at 2 o'clock and goes on till 5 o'clock. Between 8:00 and 8:20 and between 2:00 and 2:25 the classes join up for reading

aloud without a teacher. This is to allow those who have a long way to come to get here. They are allowed to arrive later. Fifth and sixth classes comprise the higher basic school. Periods are 45 minutes and breaks 10 minutes.

Fifth Class

Mathematics, 6 periods a week. Practical tasks. Use of abacus included, but not an independent subject. Calculation of cubic content.

Chinese language, 12 periods a week, of which 1 period for calligraphy and 2 periods for composition. Compositions are no longer just descriptive, but should be in the form of essays. Pupils should understand all terms in the text, read and be able to give an independent summary of a newspaper text that has been read out.

Nature study, 1 period a week. The air, soil, simple mechanical principles.

Geography, 1 period a week. China's geography, China's provinces, China's climate.

Agriculture, 2 hours a week. Climate, fertilizers, cattle, poultry, grain. Only theory.

Drawing, 1 period a week. Start water colors. First color work. First creative sketches. Theory.

Music, 1 period a week. Choral singing. Simple theory.

Gymnastics and sport, 2 periods a week. Ball games. Athletics.

Private study, 15 hours a week.

Garden work, 80 minutes a week after school hours. Looking after the school garden.

Handicraft, in spare time after school, no fixed period. Making stones for grinding color for India ink. Simple woodwork.

Homework reckoned to take one and a half hours.

Sixth Class

Mathematics, 6 periods a week. Decimal system, fractions, statistical tables, bookkeeping. Use of abacus included.

Chinese language, 12 periods a week, of which 1 for calligraphy and 2 for composition. Describe a person, a landscape. Acquire a fine style and a correct way of writing. Read aloud with the correct Peking pronunciation.

Nature study, 1 period a week. The air, soil, simple mechanical principles.

History, 2 periods a week. Only Chinese history. From Peking man to the Big Leap Forward.

Agricultural theory, 1 period a week. Climate, fertilizers, cattle, poultry, grain. Only theory.

Drawing, 1 period a week. More complicated sketches.

Gymnastics and sport, 2 periods a week. Ball games. Athletics.

Music, 1 period a week. Songs. Simple theory.

Care of garden, after school hours, 80 minutes a week.

Handicraft, in free time after school hours, no fixed period. Clay work, making color-grinding stones for India ink. Simple woodwork.

Homework reckoned to take one and a half hours a day.

Teachers stay with their classes from the first to the sixth class. The school year begins on August 1st and ends on June 20th. The school works six days a week. Together, the year's holidays amount to seventy-five days. The time of the winter holiday depends on the weather. There are eight individual holidays: two at the National Day in October, one on May 1st, one at the New Year, one on International Children's Day and three at the spring festival, if this does not coincide with the winter holiday.

The teachers are quite free during the holidays. They can go home if they wish, they can go away somewhere, they can do further study or anything else they like.

If a pupil fails in two basic subjects, like mathematics and Chinese language, he cannot move up to the next class. If a pupil fails in one basic subject, he has to be reexamined before the autumn term and can move up if he passes. If a pupil fails in three other subjects, he cannot move up. If he fails in two other subjects, he can move up. Last year, we had seven who had not moved up. A pupil who has failed to move up twice and then again gets such grades that he cannot be moved up has to leave the school. Pupils can be absent owing to sickness or with the special permission of the head.

We have no real difficulties over discipline. The only difficulty is that certain children are late for school. Of course, we have this period both in the morning and afternoon with reading aloud to give them time to get to school, and we try to get the children to help each other keep to the hours. But some of the children have a long way to come and it is difficult for them to keep to the hours.

Another difficulty is that certain children find it difficult to sit still and be quiet. Thus, in the first class there is not much discipline. There everything's more of a game. The children must think all the time that school is fun. Then gradually, as they become older, they see the necessity of work discipline, and then we require more of them.

There is a certain amount of fighting and quarreling. We try to quell this and sort it all out with discussion and persuasion. As I've said, no teacher must ever try to settle anything by striking a child. We have to check disorder by other means. And it always succeeds. Before, in the old days, schoolmasters used to beat their pupils, but then the children had no real respect for their teachers. They were just afraid of them. That was why the teachers found it difficult to keep order. Now teachers and pupils love one another, and all goes well.

Translated by Maurice Michael

CHILDHOOD IN AN INDIAN VILLAGE

WILFRED PELLETIER

One of the very important things was the relationship we had with our families. We didn't always live at home. We lived wherever we happened to be at that particular time when it got dark. If you were two or three miles away from home, then that is where you slept.

People would feed you even if they didn't know who you were. We'd spend an evening, perhaps, with an old couple, and they would tell us stories. Most of these stories were legends, and they were told to us mostly in the wintertime. In the summer people would generally take us out and we would do a number of things which in some way would allow us to learn about life and what it was all about: that is, by talking about some particular person and demonstrating what that person did. At no time, in all the years I spent there, do I ever remember anyone teaching us anything.

I have been to numerous communities across Canada, and I still do not find where Indians teach. All young children were allowed to grow, to develop, to learn. They didn't teach you that this was mommy, daddy, desk, ash tray, house, and so on. We learned about these things by listening to the words adults spoke, what they said when they were talking, and built our own kind of relationship with the article.

If you observe your children now you will see a child turn a chair over, cover it with a blanket, and use it for a house. He can relate many ways to a chair. As we get older we have only one relationship and that is to stick our rear ends on that chair. It's for no other purpose, and, in fact, we tell our kids that that is what it is, and it belongs in a corner, and don't move it out of there.

These things I remember very well. We were brought up to have a different relationship to a house and to all the things that surrounded us. That is, the values that adults placed on things in the community did not necessarily carry over into their child and lead him to place the same values on them. Children discovered the values of these things on their own, and developed their own particular relationship to them.

This is very closely related to the religion of the community, which centered entirely on man. One of the practiced ethics of the community was noninterference. No one interfered with us, and this way of living still exists today. If you go to an Indian home, the kids don't come up and bug you while you are talking to someone else. They might come and stand by you quietly, just as an adult might.

If you observe Indians someplace, they will stand quietly, and only when they are acknowledged will they speak. If they get into a group session, they will act the same way. They will sit and listen to people talk, and when they get the opportunity they will speak, but they won't cut you off or interfere. There are some who do this now, but not very many. Most of them will just wait. The whole background in the educational system was that of observing and feeling. This is how they learned.

It was a very different kind of learning situation that we were in as children. In fact, all of the things we did related to our way of life. Everything had to fit into the whole; we didn't learn things in parts. As an example: if we watched someone running an outboard motor, we would learn everything that was involved in working that motor. If someone taught someone here to do that, after he was finished he might add a safety program on top of it. This would be an additional thing. The way Indians learned it, they built in a safety program while they were learning through their observations and because their very lives depended on their doing it right.

And just as we didn't separate our learning from our way of life, we didn't separate our work from it either. The older women, for example, who used to work all day at whatever—tanning hides, and so on, didn't really think of it as work. It was a way of life. That's the real difference between the kind of society we have now, where we equate these kinds of things with work and yet will go out and play sports and enjoy it, and the kind of society I'm talking about.

Here we go and work and use maybe half or a quarter of the energy we spend playing sports, but we call it work and we feel differently about it altogether. These are the kinds of differences that exist. Indian people who had a way of life and who felt it was their way of life didn't call it work. It was part of the way they provided for their families; and they "worked" very hard.

One of the reasons, of course, why they didn't call it "work" was that they didn't have any foremen. As I mentioned before, there wasn't any kind of a vertical structure in the community. In these communities what existed was a sharing of power. In spite of what everybody says, we really didn't have chiefs, that is, people who were bosses. We had medicine men, who were wise men. The rest were leaders in particular ways. They weren't leaders as we look at them today. It was a different kind of leadership in that the person who was leader had special abilities, say in fishing or hunting. He took the leadership that day, and then discarded the leadership when he was finished with the job. He had power only for the time he wanted to do something. That power came in all forms of all the things he did in the community, so that he used power only for the things he wanted to do, and then he immediately shed it so that someone else could pick it up and it could change hands several times in the community in a day or a week or whatever.

Only in times of war and disaster was a vertical structure used. The war chief would designate various jobs to various people and use that vertical structure. This was only in times of danger. Otherwise, it was horizontal. My grandfather one time told me this, although it didn't sink in until just a few years ago, that to have power is destructive. You'll be destructive if you have power because if people don't join you, then you will destroy them. I forgot this and dug around for power and began to lose friends. I was making decisions for people even with the background I have.

Now I have such a problem fighting this thing off, because people are always putting me in a position where I have power. They say I am director of the Institute of Indian Studies. This is not true. I'm just at Rochdale College. Where I am everyone makes up their own minds in terms of what they want to do, and they do those things, and if I can be of assistance, then I assist. I've got my own thing that I hope to do. One of the things that I'm interested in is the kind of lives that the young Indian people now at Rochdale live—what is happening to them in the city.

The city has special problems for them as it had for me. For many of them were raised in Indian homes, where the attitude is that no child ever should be rejected.

In an Indian home, if a child's face is dirty or his diaper is wet, he is picked up by anyone—the mother or father or whoever comes into the house. He is never rejected. And they don't stick children in cribs, where they can only look in one direction—up. The child generally sits or stands (often tied in), so he can relate to the world in all directions. And children are fed whenever they are hungry. They are never allowed to be in want. Whatever is wanted is given to them. If a child wants to play with something, it is always placed in his hand. No one would think of putting a rattle slightly out of reach, so he would try to grab it and be aggressive. No one would think of feeding the baby only at set times. What follows this approach in terms of attitudes and way of life is immense. The child's nature is very strongly influenced in the first four or five years. The children become very noncompetitive. They have no need to compete.

The whole situation changes, however, when they go out into the world, where the attitudes and values are totally different. A world, further, in which their values are not acceptable, where for many of us as children we were not even permitted to speak our own language. Of course, we still tried to speak our own language, but we were punished for it. Four or five years ago they were still stripping the kids of their clothes up around Kenora and beating them for speaking their own language. It is probably still happening in many other institutions today. I was punished several times for speaking Indian not only on the school grounds but off the school grounds and on the street, and I lived across from the school. Almost in front of my own door my first language was forbidden me; and yet when I went into the house, my parents spoke Indian.

Our language is so important to us as a people. Our language and language structure are related to our whole way of life. How beautiful that picture language is where they only tell you the beginning and the end, and you fill in everything, and they allow you to feel how you want to feel.

Here we manipulate and twist things around and get you to hate a guy. The Indian doesn't do that. He'll just say that some guy got into an accident, and he won't give you any details. From there on you just explore as far as you want to. You'll say, "What happened?" and he'll tell you a little more. "Did he go through the windshield?" "Yep!" He only answers questions. All of the in-between you fill in for yourself as you see it.

We are losing that feeling when we lose our language at school. We are taught English, not Indian, as our first language. And that changes our relationship with our parents. All of a sudden we begin saying to our parents, "You're stupid." We have begun to equate literacy with learning, and this is the first step down. It is we who are going down and not our parents, and because of that separation we are going down lower and lower on the rung because it is we who are rejecting our parents; they are not rejecting us. The parents know that, but they are unable to do anything about it. And we take on the values, and the history of somebody else.

And part of the reason our parents say so little is that that's their way. They don't teach like white people; they let their children make their own decisions. The closest they ever got to formal teaching was to tell us stories. Let me give you an example.

We had been out picking blueberries one time, and while sitting around this guy told us this story. The idea was that he wanted to get us to wash up—to wash our feet because we had been tramping through this brush all day long. He talked about a warrior who really had a beautiful body. He was very well built, and he used to grease himself and take care of his body.

One day this warrior was out, and he ran into a group of other people whom he had never seen before. They started to chase him. He had no problem because he was in such good shape. He was fooling around and playing with them because he was such a good runner. He ran over hills and over rocks, teasing them. Then he ran into another group. The first group gave up the chase. But now he had to run away from this other group, and he was fooling around doing the same thing with them. All of a sudden he ran into a third group. He ran real hard and all of a sudden he fell. He tried to get up and he couldn't. He spoke to his feet and said, "What's wrong with you? I'm going to get killed if you don't get up and get going."

They said, "That's all right. You can comb your hair and grease your body and look after your legs and arms, but you never did anything for us. You never washed us or cleaned us or greased us or nothing."

He promised to take better care of the feet if they would get up and run, and so they did.

This is one of the stories we were told, and we went up and washed our feet right away and then went to bed. Maybe this happens among other ethnic groups, I don't know, but this is the kind of learning we had. I will never forget the kinds of things we learned, because to me it all belongs to me. It isn't something that someone says is so; it's mine.

I'd want to go hunting, and the guys would know I couldn't get across the stream because it was flooded, but they wouldn't say anything. They'd let me go, and I'd tell them I'd see them later where the rocks are, and they'd say OK knowing all this time I couldn't get through. But they wouldn't tell me that. They'd let me experience it. And I'm grateful to these people for allowing me to have this kind of exploration-learning situation. Secondly, of course, the fact is that maybe I could have gotten across where they couldn't, discovered something different, a method that was new. I think this kind of learning situation is one of the really important things that Indians have today and which could contribute to the society we have today. That is, a learning situation *for people,* instead of teaching or information-giving.

"Santa Clo" Comes to La Cuchilla

ABELARDO DÍAZ ALFARO

A flash of red bunting fluttering on a bamboo pole marked the location of Peyo Mercé's little schoolhouse. A long partition divided the tiny school into two classrooms. In one of these a new teacher, Mr. Johnny Rosas, now ruled the roost.

Since that ill-fated day when Peyo Mercé had made the district superintendent, Mr. Rogelio Escalera, look foolish in public, the latter thought it advisable to assign another teacher to the parish of La Cuchilla, one who might impress upon old Peyo the latest educational techniques and shine the beacon of progress upon that unenlightened backwoods.

He summoned Johnny Rosas—an up-and-coming fellow, just graduated and recently returned from the customary whirl in the United States—to his office, and solemnly declared, "Look here, Johnny, I'm sending you out to La Cuchilla so you can bring them up to date on teaching methods. That old codger Peyo doesn't have the foggiest notion of such things. He's at least forty years behind the times. Try to change their ways and, above all, you must teach them English, lots and lots of English!"

And so it happened that one day Peyo saw an old and jaded mare jogging up the hill with the fledgling teacher on its back. He felt no grudge against Johnny. He even felt a little pity and muttered to himself, "In time life will leave her maze of furrows in him, as the plough does upon the land." And he ordered some farm urchins to take the harness off the mare and put her out to pasture.

Peyo knew that life in the hills was going to be tough on the young upstart. Meals are poor: rice and beans, garlic dressing, smoked fish, salt cod, thin soup, hardtack, and lots of water to stretch things out. Roads are almost impassable and always full of mud holes. People take baths in the creek and use rain water for drinking. Peyo had to plan his lessons by the flickering light of a lantern or a tallow candle.

When night fell, Johnny Rosas felt bored. The mountains grew dark and eerie. Blinking here and there, a dim and sallow bead of light would hang suspended on the gloomy monotony of the landscape. Crickets pierced the heart of the night. A rooster broke off his slow and quavering crowing. In the distance, a dog dragged out a doleful howl at the blossoming stars. And Peyo Mercé would trot off to poker and dominoes at the general store.

One day Johnny Rosas said to Peyo, "This parish is very backward. We must overhaul it. It's essential to bring in new things and throw out the dead wood, the old traditions. Remember the words of superintendent Escalera, 'Down with tradition!' We must teach lots of English and copy the customs of the Americans."

And Peyo, without getting overwrought, squeezed out these words, "You're right, English is good and we need it. But, bless our soul, we can't even speak Spanish correctly! And hunger turns children into halfwits. The fox once said to the snail, 'Before you can run, you must learn to walk.' " But Johnny didn't grasp the meaning of his words.

The tobacco farms became a little livelier; the Christmas holidays drew near. Peyo had already observed with pleasure a few of his pupils making rustic guitars out of cedar and rosewood. These fiestas brought back happy memories of bygone days. Days of carnival masquerades and dancing in the conga lines; days when the tobacco crop sold well and racks of roast pork were sent to the neighbors as tokens of fellowship. He still seemed to hear the old ditty that went:

> The man is no mouse
> who lives in that house;
> he's high-born I feel
> since the doors are of steel.

Johnny suddenly yanked Peyo out of his reverie saying, "This year, Santa Claus will make his debut at La Cuchilla. This business of the Three Wise Men bringing gifts is getting to be old hat. Folks in San Juan hardly bother with it anymore. The custom belongs to the past. I'll invite Mr. Escalera to the party; it will give him great pleasure." Unperturbed, Peyo scratched his head and answered, "If you want to kill the goose that laid the golden eggs, that's up to you. As for me, I'm just a hick who never left the backwoods, so the feast of the Wise Men is dear to my heart. We hayseeds have a nose for these things, as we do for codfish cakes."

Johnny, anxious to pave the way for Santa's "Gala Première" at La Cuchilla, cooked up some class projects. He showed his students a poster of Santa Claus riding a sleigh pulled by reindeer. But Peyo, who happened to be standing at the threshold of the door between the classrooms, saw a different image: a pale-faced old peasant sitting on a palm-leaf sledge dragged by a team of goats. Mr. Rosas asked his rustic fledglings, "Who is this personage?" And Benito, full of the devil and clever as they come, answered, "Misteh, dat's de Old Year, painted red." Johnny was dumbfounded by the ignorance of his little flock and at the same time felt indignation at Peyo Mercé's negligence.

Christmas Eve arrived and all the parents were invited. In his classroom, Peyo staged a traditional fiesta which came off with flying colors. Some of the kids sang local ballads and carols accompanying themselves on their hand-made guitars. To cap things off, the Three Wise Men appeared, while Simón, the old troubadour, rhymed away with: "The Wise Men wander far and near. / We farm folk just stay right here." Candies and rice pudding were passed around and the kids exchanged "tricks or treats." Then Peyo asked his students to file into the adjacent classroom, where Johnny Rosas had a surprise for them, and had even invited Mr. Escalera, the superintendent.

In the center of the room stood an artificial Christmas tree. Red streamers dangled from shelf to shelf. Hung on the walls were tiny green wreaths with a scarlet berry in the middle. A sign, in frosted white letters, read "Merry Christmas"—in English. Artificial snow was sprinkled over everything. The spectators, who had never seen the like of it before, stared at all this in astonishment. Mr. Escalera was visibly pleased.

Some of the children climbed on top of an improvised platform and arranged themselves to spell out "Santa Claus." One of them narrated the life of Papa Noël, followed by a chorus of kids singing "Jingle Bells" while tinkling away at a string of little chimes. The parents looked at each other, bewildered. Mr. Rosas disappeared for a moment. Whereupon superintendent Escalera made a speech congratulating everyone for the fine little party and for having in their midst such an energetic and progressive teacher as Mr. Rosas. Escalera then requested the most profound silence from the audience, for soon they were to meet a strange, mysterious personage. Instantly, a tiny chorus burst out singing:

> Santa Claus is coming here . . .
> Hear his sled as it draws near!
> Clip, clop! Clip, clop!

Suddenly the figure of Santa Claus materialized in the doorway—a red and white apparition with a huge sack on its shoulder. In cavernous tones, it boomed out, "Here is Santa! Merry Christmas to you all!"—in English.

A howl of terror shook the room. Some of the farmers started leaping out of the windows. Toddlers began to bawl, clutching the skirts of the womenfolk, who in turn were fleeing in all directions like stampeding cattle. Everyone tried to escape. Mr. Rosas ran after them, trying to explain that it was he who had dressed up in such weird garb. But this only made the screaming louder and the panic more intense. An old crone crossed herself and said, "God help us! Bless me if it ain't ol' Satan himself, talkin' in American!"

The superintendent made useless efforts to calm the crowd, shouting like a fiend, "Stop! Stop! Quit acting like typical Puerto Rican bumpkins! Santa Claus is a good and humane man!"

In the distance one could hear a screaming chorus of stampeding farmers. And Mr. Escalera, noticing that Peyo Mercé had stood through the whole thing sphinx-like and indifferent, vented all his rage upon him, berating him at the top of his voice, "You, Peyo Mercé! It's your fault that such barbarism should exist here in the middle of the twentieth century!"

And, cool as a cucumber, Peyo replied, "Mr. Escalera, it's hardly my fault if this newfangled saint of yours doesn't happen to be included in the index of Puerto Rican saints."

Translated by Julio de la Torre

Our baby's gone

Father snores as his wife gets into her dressing gown,
Picks up the letter that's lying there,
Standing alone at the top of the stairs,
She breaks down and cries to her husband,
Daddy, our baby's gone.
Why should she treat us so thoughtlessly,
How could she do this to me.
She (We never thought of ourselves)
is leaving (Never a thought for ourselves)
home (We struggled hard all our lives to get by)
She's leaving home after living alone
for so many years. Bye, bye.

From "She's Leaving Home" by John Lennon
and Paul McCartney for the Beatles (England).

She's Leaving Home

JOHN LENNON and PAUL McCARTNEY

Wednesday morning at five o'clock as the day begins,
Silently closing her bedroom door,
Leaving the note that she hoped would say more,
She goes downstairs to the kitchen,
clutching her handkerchief,
quietly turning the backdoor key;
stepping outside she is free.
She (We gave her most of our lives)
is leaving (Sacrificed most of our lives)
home (We gave her everything money could buy)
She's leaving home after living alone
for so many years. Bye, bye.

Father snores as his wife gets into her dressing gown
Picks up the letter that's lying there
Standing alone at the top of the stairs
She breaks down and cries to her husband
Daddy, our baby's gone.
Why should she treat us so thoughtlessly
How could she do this to me.
She (We never thought of ourselves)
is leaving (Never a thought for ourselves)
home (We struggled hard all our lives to get by)
She's leaving home after living alone
for so many years. Bye, bye.

Friday morning at nine o'clock she is far away,
Waiting to keep the appointment she made,
meeting a man from the motor trade.
She (What did we do that was wrong)
is leaving (We didn't know it was wrong)
home (Fun is the one thing that money can't buy)
Something inside that was always denied
for so many years. Bye, bye.
She's leaving home. Bye, bye.

With God's Blessing, MOM

JOSÉ CARLOS CAVALCANTI BORGES

I

My dear son,

Your father's headache is a little better. Mr. Quincas, the new druggist at the corner, says it might be albumen. What do you think?

Someone told me that you're going with a girl. They said it was serious.

My son, I don't think it is time yet for you to get involved with anyone. Your father and I talked it over, and he thinks just as I do. You haven't graduated yet. Even after graduation you'll find that life is very difficult nowadays. I didn't really believe it about you and this girl being serious. But anyway, don't be angry with me for offering a bit of advice.

Little Bernardo has been studying more. The teacher says he seems to be developing a taste for it. (But I wish he wasn't so crazy about music. He goes to all the band rehearsals at the Euterpe Club.)

Do you think it would help your father if he went to Recife for an examination?

Be sensible, my son.

With God's blessing,
Mom

II

My dear son,

I was greatly relieved by what you wrote in your letter. Everybody here has been catching the grippe. I'm glad to say that your father's headache is no worse. He had a touch of the grippe, but it was mostly in the nose.

The person who told me about your girl must have thought it was true. I trust her implicitly. She is the sister of a lady who lives near you.

She wouldn't tell me the girl's name but she said it was someone I was acquainted with and that if I knew the whole truth I wouldn't like it.

But now I'm happy. I know it's not what she thinks and that it's nothing but a silly flirtation.

Be careful, my son. You aren't rich. Your father is advanced in years, and his greatest happiness would be to see you graduated and with a good job. My greatest happiness, too.

Mr. Quincas offered to bring it to you, and so I'm taking advantage of his kindness to send you this dried beef. It was bought on Saturday. Your father picked the kind you like.

I almost forgot the big news. The mayor said he was going to open a school and promised Ceminha a job as teacher. She is very happy. So are we.

With God's blessing,
Mom

III

My dear son,

It's two weeks since I last wrote you. Ceminha has the grippe. Little Bernardo got a bad cold. He caught it one night when it was raining and he went to a rehearsal at the Euterpe Club. Your father forbade him to go any more until he's older.

You said it wasn't at all important about you and Lélé, but I'm wondering if you yourself realize how serious it might be. Going to the movies with her. Walking on the beach with her as if you were engaged.

Is it really not serious, my son?

You may be very fond of her. But, my son, I'm going to speak frankly, because I'm your mother. Don't you know what people here and in Recife say about Lélé's mother? There are so many girls and you have to pick Palmira's daughter. Don't you know that Palmira is practically separated from her husband? The only reason he doesn't actually leave her is that she has money. Her daughter may have many good points but, after all, she lives with her mother, she was brought up by her mother, and she must have learned her mother's ways. The girl may like you and may seem very nice, but later on she will probably turn out bad like her mother. I'm speaking to you frankly.

Your father says that Ceminha's job in the school is definite. I'm not so sure. I don't trust these politicians.

Think carefully about what I told you. Would you really want to marry into Palmira's family?

With God's blessing,
Mom

92

IV

My dear son,

I have been crying. Even your father is becoming suspicious. You write one thing but you do something else. Do you think people here don't know what goes on in Recife? Well, you're very much mistaken. You've been going swimming at the beach with Lélé. You've been walking on Nova Street with her and her mother, as if you were officially engaged already. All that's missing is the ring. My son, do you want to ruin your life? Don't you see that this attachment is not right for you? I made a promise to the good Lord of what I'll do if he saves you. I'm sure he will.

Tomorrow or the day after, the postmaster's sister is going to Recife to spend a few days. I'm going to take advantage of the opportunity to send you some cookies. If they are soggy when they get there, ask permission to put them in the stove for a few minutes and they'll get nice and crisp.

Why don't you spend more time studying that subject in which you got a low grade?

My son, I write you with tears in my eyes, for I know what you have in store for you. Don't have anything more to do with that girl. She will ruin your life, my son.

With God's blessing,
Mom

V

My dear son,

I sent the cookies as I promised. Remember what to do if they're soggy. Your father woke up this morning with a terrible headache. Don't have anything more to do with that girl.

With God's blessing,
Mom

VI

My dear son,

I was happy to get your letter. I know now that you haven't forgotten your mother entirely. But I notice you don't say anything about you and that brazenfaced girl. I am worried, my son. If you don't want to tell me about it, it must be serious. (I heard that Palmira's husband left for Rio de Janeiro. I don't know whether it's true.) Why don't you write me about you and the girl?

Take your mother's advice, my son. All that I want in the whole world is your happiness.

Yesterday I felt terribly ashamed. At the novena, Maria Pia came up and asked me if you were getting married to Palmira's daughter. She heard it somewhere. I didn't know what to say. All through the novena and all night long I sobbed until I nearly choked. I tell you this because you ought to know how I am suffering.

You must not think that your father and I don't want you to fall in love and get married. But a boy like you deserves a different kind of girl, a fine girl, a girl of good upbringing. Besides, isn't it a little early for you to be thinking of marriage? Don't let yourself become engaged to that girl, my son. It's for your own good, believe me.

Little Bernardo wants you to buy "The Art of Music" for him to study. He says they have it in the bookstores in Recife. Your father will send you the money as soon as he knows of someone going to Recife.

May the good Lord watch over you, my son.

Mom

VII

My dear son,

For the past three days your father has been unable to sleep. His head hurts him all the time. Mr. Quincas doesn't want him to take any more aspirin. Your father hardly eats a thing.

I found out something very sad today—your father knows everything. He has been worrying in silence for a long time without saying a word to me about it. Yesterday, when your letter came, he asked me to read it to him. His migraine is so bad he can't focus his eyes. When I finished, he said, "I was beginning to feel a little better, Iáiá, because something told me that in that letter João would tell us he had broken off with that brazenfaced girl."

Poor man! I felt so sorry for him. I had never mentioned the subject to him because I wanted your father to get well.

Ceminha has been helping me a great deal. She was studying to begin her teaching but these days she has no time for it.

Do you know of any medicine that might help your father? He won't take injections. Mr. Quincas means well but his drugstore is worse than when Mr. Lobo was there.

I can't wait for the holidays to come, my son.

With God's blessing,
Mom

VIII

My dear son,

We're all so happy here to learn that you're coming on the first of December. It is the most joyful news we could have.

Is it really true, my son? Is your friendship for Lélé and Palmira really not serious?

Today the mayor was at the internal revenue office and he spoke to your father. He was very roundabout, but the gist of it was that he isn't going to appoint Ceminha as teacher in the new school. He had a request from a municipal judge who wanted the job for his niece. You don't know her, she came to live here only about a month ago. The judge has a cousin who was a congressman. The mayor promised to have a position for Ceminha in another school that he's going to open next year near the slaughterhouse.

Little Bernardo is already accompanying the band on his trumpet. Your father pretends he doesn't approve, but almost every night he stands at the door of the Euterpe Club and listens.

Is it really not serious, my son?

Study hardest the subjects in which you are weakest.

I hear that neckties with a solid color are the thing to wear now. I've been saving a piece of blue silk. It's very pretty. For a lining I'll use one that I took from an old necktie of your father's.

With God's blessing,
Mom

I put this letter in an envelope, but luckily I did not seal it. This evening when your father got back from the Euterpe, he found Ceminha talking with a young man. He didn't say anything to her but he wasn't happy about it and he told me he was going to find out who the young man is. Tomorrow I'll have a talk with her.

Mom

Translated by William T. Grossman

On Children

KAHLIL GIBRAN

And a woman who held a babe against her bosom said,
Speak to us of Children.

And he said:

Your children are not your children.

They are the sons and daughters of Life's longing for
itself.

They come through you but not from you,

And though they are with you yet they belong not to you.

You may give them your love but not your thoughts,

For they have their own thoughts.

You may house their bodies but not their souls,

For their souls dwell in the house of tomorrow, which
you cannot visit, not even in your dreams.

You may strive to be like them, but seek not to make
them like you.

For life goes not backward nor tarries with yesterday.

You are the bows from which your children as living
arrows are sent forth.

The archer sees the mark upon the path of the infinite,
and he bends you with his might that his arrows may go swift
and far.

Let your bending in the archer's hand be for gladness;

For even as he loves the arrow that flies, so he loves also
the bow that is stable.

SONS AND LOVERS

RICK HORNSEY

I do not think our fathers ever met
but we know from their stories
that their camaraderie was strong.
They slapped backs,
twisted wrists, shot rabbits,
fondled rumble-seat girls,
fought Hitler,
thickened their livers with whisky
and their hands with work
all before they were twenty-five.

We could not have been their comrades
had we known them then.
What would they have thought
of spending a whole morning
watching the eyelids of a sleeping girl
or leaving half a beer
to go outside to make angels
in the new snow.
What sort of legacy is that
to give to children?

Once Upon a Time

GABRIEL OKARA

Once upon a time, son,
they used to laugh with their hearts
and laugh with their eyes;
but now they only laugh with their teeth,
while their ice-block-cold eyes
search behind my shadow.

There was a time indeed
they used to shake hands with their hearts;
but that's gone, son.
Now they shake hands without hearts
while their left hands search
my empty pockets.

"Feel at home," "Come again,"
they say, and when I come
again and feel
at home, once, twice,
there will be no thrice—
for then I find doors shut on me.

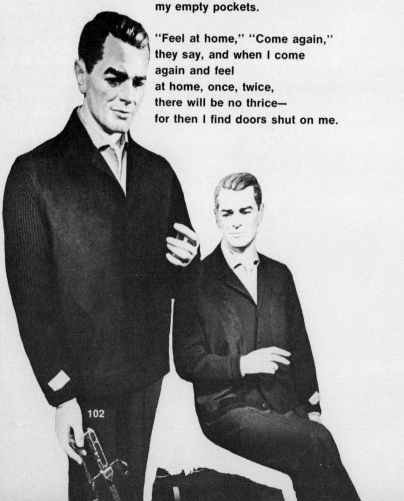

So I have learned many things, son.
I have learned to wear many faces
like dresses—homeface,
officeface, streetface, hostface, cocktailface,
with all their conforming smiles
like a fixed portrait smile.

And I have learned too
to laugh with only my teeth
and shake hands without my heart.
I have also learned to say, "Good-by,"
when I mean "Goodriddance";
to say "Glad to meet you,"
without being glad; and to say "It's been
nice talking to you," after being bored.

But believe me, son.
I want to be what I used to be
when I was like you. I want
to unlearn all these muting things.
Most of all, I want to relearn
how to laugh, for my laugh in the mirror
shows only my teeth like a snake's bare fangs!

So show me, son,
how to laugh; show me how
I used to laugh and smile
once upon a time when I was like you.

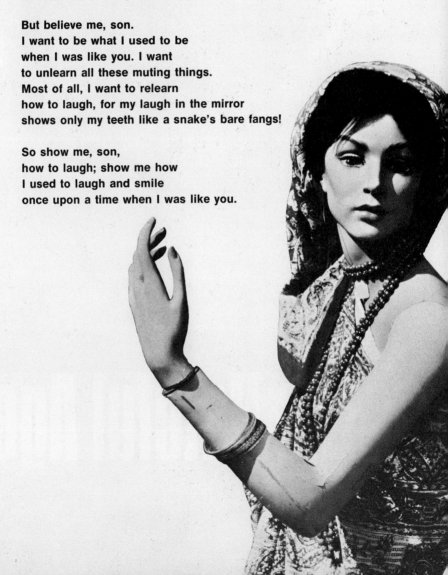

from

The Hateful Age

NIWA FUMIO

I

Almost every morning when Sachiko made Umé's bed, she would come upon some object—a button, an envelope, a ball of string—that Granny had stolen and carefully sequestered under the bedding. The fact that these things would eventually be found did not stop the old woman; the habit of stealing had become far too deeply ingrained for the most strenuous reprimands to have effect. Moreover, there seemed to be little use in lecturing her, as Umé apparently failed to hear or to understand; she simply stared ahead with a blank, bewildered look, and Sachiko assumed that in her old age Umé was becoming deaf. However, the children were not so easily fooled, and they took great delight in exposing their great-grandmother's pretence.

"Would you like a raw onion, Granny?" said one of the little boys, standing at the other end of the room, and speaking in a low voice which would normally fail to make the slightest impression on Umé. Onions were the old lady's favorite food and she immediately rose to the bait.

"An onion?" she said. "Oh yes, I'd love one."

"I caught you that time, Granny!" cried the boy, and ran out of the room laughing.

A few days later occurred an incident which reduced still further Umé's popularity in her new home. The children were playing with toy dragonflies and one of the missiles by chance flew off in the wrong direction and struck the old woman on the forehead. Crying out, she glared into the garden, and there caught sight of the young culprit. In a tone that would have sent shivers down the spine of a tough samurai, let alone a small child, she screamed, "Curse you, you little fiend! Curse you, I say!" Taking from the folds of her dress a recently stolen dishcloth, she began to wipe the blood from her forehead.

At lunchtime a few days later, the boy said to his father, "Granny's keeping that cloth with the blood on it."

"Really?" said Minobé. "Why?"

At that Umé again took out the dishcloth from her dress and held it up for all to see. In the center was a dark stain which could be recognized as blood.

"I'm keeping this as a reminder," she said. "I'll show it to people so that they'll realize how I've been treated here."

"You know perfectly well that it was a mistake, Granny," said Minobé.

"I'm not so sure about that," Umé said. She had abandoned her usual respectful tone and spoke defiantly, almost harshly.

"All right," said Minobé, "if that's going to be your attitude, I can be just as disagreeable as anyone else."

At once Umé lowered her head, and gave out an old woman's cackle.

"Of course it was a mistake," she said. "I was only joking."

Staring at Umé, Minobé suddenly remembered the Confucian teaching on filial piety and respect for one's elders. Was it possible that the Master had had sly, wicked old women like this in mind when he expounded his noble teachings? To respect an insensitive old woman like Umé, conscious as she was of only the physical aspects of life, was like worshiping a stone idol! Umé had become just a body, in which it was impossible to detect the slightest trace of soul, spirit, conscience or anything that makes human beings worthy of respect. Her greatest worry in life was that her grandchildren or great-grandchildren might be getting better food than herself.

To be sure, thought Minobé, there were people like Kōda Rohan, the great scholar, whose intellectual powers remained unimpaired until his death at the age of eighty. Such people, indeed, seemed as they grew older to become constantly more sensitive and intelligent. They were one in a thousand! The remaining nine hundred and ninety-nine were destined to become distasteful, useless lumps of flesh, the scourge of relatives and a burden to society.

There was hardly a family in Japan that did not suffer from the system in which old people had to be either cared for by their children or committed to primitive and sinister institutions. People had been complaining for years, but the traditional family system still lingered on, with all its inefficiency, hypocrisy, sentimentality, and injustice. It was high time for something to be done—not by sociologists, but by people all over Japan who were themselves suffering from these out-of-date traditions.

II

Not long afterward, Minobé was able to take over a house in Tokyo from a friend. In the new house Umé was assigned a small room of her own next to the toilet. Here she would sit quietly and give herself over to the new and particularly annoying habit that she had acquired since her return to Tokyo: taking any piece of material she could lay hands on—clothes, towels or sheets—she would systematically tear it to shreds. In the case of clothes, she would first rip the material from the hem upward into strips about one centimeter in width, and then start on the sleeves; by the time she had finished, the pieces were so small that they could not even be used for dusters. Her usual expression while she did this was one of guileless vacancy, though as she tore up a particularly long piece or sat contemplating a huge pile of tatters, one could observe that an enigmatic smile would play on her lips.

No one could make out the origin of this new quirk. Was it that Umé, whose entire youth had been devoted to the art of needlework (one of the few accomplishments then considered suitable for women of breeding), felt in some paradoxical way that by tearing material she was at least persevering in her speciality, even though she was now too old to do so constructively? Or was it that in an access of spite she had decided that none of her clothes or other possessions should ever go to this family which had treated her so heartlessly in her declining years? Or was it just the sheer joy of vandalism? The result, in any case, was that despite Sachiko's best efforts, Umé's wardrobe had soon dwindled to nothing. Because of the strict rationing it was impossible to replace the shredded garments, so Sachiko had to give her grandmother some of her own castoff clothes. With their modern pattern and bright colors, they produced a somewhat ludicrous effect on the old lady. In the end they too were, of course, torn to bits.

"It's funny how Granny only likes things with salt," said Sachiko one day. "Most old people like sweet things, but she'll only eat things when they're salted or spicy."

"Let's hope she doesn't get pickled and live forever!" said Minobé.

"Yes," said Sachiko, "the kindest thing she could do for herself and everyone else would be to die. Why do you suppose she goes on living like this?"

Minobé shrugged his shoulders.

"In the Far East, longevity's supposed to be a wonderful thing," he answered. "For some reason it's considered a feat to grow very old, even though one doesn't have the slightest pleasure in being alive and is just a nuisance to everyone around. Take that old dog next door. Its owners go around boasting to everyone that they've got a dog who's lived to be fifteen. And yet the poor old thing is blind and lame and should have died years ago. Evidently in Japan we can't even let animals die at the proper time!

"The fact is that once people are wrecks, like Granny, life becomes a spiteful force which turns on its owner, as if to punish him for hanging on to it so long. The blessings of old age, indeed! All Granny really cares about is eating, but because she's over sixty, the Government will only let her have a reduced ration. That's what I mean by life turning on people if they live too long. And when they finally do die, what sort of memory do they leave behind? Just the memory of their last ugly, unhappy years. Granny once was a lovely woman, to judge from her photos, but what we'll remember is a hideous, wicked old hag. Surely people should fade out like music, leaving a beautiful melody in the air."

Almost all day, apart from meal times, Umé lay half-asleep by the charcoal brazier in the living room. At night, however, she was wide awake. As soon as the family had gone to sleep, she would wander out into the passage and start complaining raucously of hunger. Finally someone would have to get up and give her a piece of bread, a potato or a rice-ball.

As soon as Umé awoke from one of her naps, she would start wailing, "Oh, I'm hungry! I'm dying of hunger! Bring me something to eat for pity's sake—a rice-ball, an onion pickle, anything. Only hurry!" Sometimes there were variations: "Help, the fire's gone out! I'm dying of cold. Come and light the fire, someone!" or "Water, water! For mercy's sake, Master, bring me a glass of water!"

An especially irritating habit was her referring to people in terms of exaggerated obsequiousness, as if to imply that only so could she persuade them to help her. Thus Minobé became "Master," Sachiko was "Madam" or "Mistress" and her great-grandchildren "young sirs." As he stood painting in his studio room, Minobé would hear her shrill voice: "Oh, my dear Mistress, may I crave a few grains of rice to calm my hunger?" or "Young sir, have mercy on an old woman and bring a glass of water!" Despite his resolutions, Minobé would sometimes fling his paintbrush to the floor.

Her pilfering continued, and indeed had grown worse. If, on waking, she saw no one about, she would hurry over to one of the cupboards and take whatever she could find. Formerly, stolen objects had always been retrieved in her room, but Umé's pilfering had become far more serious since she had taken to tearing things to pieces.

III

One day the children discovered a large piece of fresh bread in the dustbin and brought it to their mother.

"If that isn't the limit!" said Sachiko. "This is the piece I gave Granny a few hours ago. I know she doesn't like this cheap rationed bread, but it's all any of us can get these days. And I salted it specially for her."

She went into Umé's room and scolded her severely, but the old lady denied all knowledge of the bread. The following day a whole bowl of rice was found in the dustbin.

"How can anyone throw away rice these days when millions are starving!" cried Sachiko, glaring at Umé. "Such waste deserves to be punished."

"Good gracious!" said Umé. "Who could have done such a thing?"

"You know perfectly well it was you, Granny! You're the only one who throws things like this in the dustbin."

"Mercy me, no!" said Umé indignantly. "I'd rather die than throw rice away. It's a sacrilege. Let me tell you, I'd like to get my hands on whoever did it. . . ."

At this point Sachiko gave up.

In the evening she mentioned the matter to Minobé. "She's lost all judgment, hasn't she? If she wanted to get rid of the rice, all she had to do was to throw it down the toilet and none of us would have been the wiser. This way we were bound to find out."

"She was probably furious because the rice was cold," said Minobé.

"We all had cold rice today," said Sachiko. "She had the same as the rest of us."

"Yes, but nothing will ever convince her that we aren't getting better food than she is. I expect she purposely put the rice where we'd find it, as a sort of protest."

"I wonder if her mental powers are up to that," said Sachiko.

"When it comes to food, they certainly are!" said Minobé. "Look at that awful habit she's got of bowing and scraping to us all, in the hope that we'll give her extra things to eat."

"Yes, I suppose she'll sink to anything to fill her belly. It's all that she lives for these days. It's as if she were under a curse! It really makes me sad, you know, when I think that she's my own grandmother."

When visitors came to the house, they would invariably be startled by the sudden sight of old Umé, with her weird, white, wrinkled face and fuzzy hair.

"Are they from Echigo?" she would ask, and having been assured to the contrary, she would raise a piteous cry, "Oh, I'm so hungry! For mercy's sake, good people, let me have something to eat! I haven't had a morsel since last night. Help! I'm starving!"

Sachiko and Minobé would then be obliged to explain matters to the bewildered guests.

IV

In his spare time Minobé unpacked the numerous trunks and cases which they had brought from the country. One day he came upon a small photograph which had lain hidden for years among some old papers. He examined it for a moment, then took it to Umé's room.

"I expect you'll remember this, Granny," he said.

Old Umé was busy tearing to pieces a pair of her great-grandson's pants. She was having some trouble with the elastic band around the waist. She looked up and took the photograph which Minobé handed her, and suddenly a strange choked cry escaped her throat.

"Oh, oh, I've missed her so terribly! It's my darling little girl. My only daughter! I've missed her for so long!"

She put her hand to her forehead and rubbed her cheek against the photograph of the daughter, who had died over thirty years before; her whole body was shaking.

"Why did you have to leave me? Life has never been the same since. How I miss you!"

Minobé was deeply moved. Now at last he seemed to have discovered beneath all the physical and moral ugliness with which age had marked old Umé, a human heart that felt and suffered. Bowing his head he left the room. He did not want to intrude on her terrible grief.

As soon as he closed the door, the sound of sobbing appeared suddenly to stop. He stood listening in the passage. There seemed to him something ominous about this silence following directly on the old lady's desperate weeping. Opening the door quietly, Minobé looked in. With an air of rapt concentration, Umé was removing the rubber band from her great-grandson's pants. The photograph lay discarded upon a heap of tattered cloth.

Translated by Ivan Morris

"You've failed, utterly!"

Beautiful Old Age

D. H. LAWRENCE

It ought to be lovely to be old
to be full of the peace that comes of experience
and wrinkled ripe fulfillment.

The wrinkled smile of completeness that follows a life
lived undaunted and unsoured with accepted lies.
If people lived without accepting lies
they would ripen like apples, and be scented like pippins
in their old age.

Soothing, old people should be, like apples
when one is tired of love.
Fragrant like yellowing leaves, and dim with the soft
stillness and satisfaction of autumn.

And a girl should say,
It must be wonderful to live and grow old.
Look at my mother, how rich and still she is!—

And a young man should think: By Jove
my father has faced all weathers, but it's been a life!—

from

THE DARK CHILD

CAMARA LAYE

When I returned to Kouroussa with my proficiency certificate in my pocket and feeling, I must confess, a little swollen with success, I was greeted with open arms, with the same eagerness and affection that had awaited me at the end of every school year. This time I had a fresh sense of pride. On the road from the station to our concession there had been the most enthusiastic demonstrations of welcome, and they had all sprung from the same love and friendship. But while my parents embraced me—my mother was probably rejoicing more over my return than over the diploma—my mind was uneasy, especially so far as she was concerned.

Before I had left Conakry the director of the school had sent for me and asked me if I would like to go to France to finish my studies. I had blithely answered yes, but I had said it without having consulted my parents, without having consulted my mother. My uncles in Conakry had told me that it was a unique opportunity and that I didn't deserve to live if I turned it down. What would my parents say? Especially my mother? I did not feel at all comfortable. I waited until the first ecstatic greetings were over and then announced loudly, as if the news would be a source of delight to everyone:

"And that's not all. The director wants to send me to France!"

"To France?" my mother said.

I saw her face stiffen.

"Yes. I'm to be given a scholarship. It won't cost us anything."

"As if the cost mattered! So you're going to leave us again."

"Well, I'm not sure."

I could see that what I had been afraid of had happened. I had been too hasty in saying yes to the director.

"You're not going!" she said.

"No. But it wouldn't be for more than a year."

"A year?" said my father. "A year? That's not so very long."

"What?" my mother broke in sharply. "A year isn't so very long? For the last four years our son has been with us only on holidays, and you stand there and say a year is not so very long?"

"Well . . ." my father began.

"No, no! He's not going. That's that!"

"All right," my father said. "We won't speak of it again. This is the day of his return, his day of success. Let us rejoice. We'll talk about the other matter later."

We said no more, for people were beginning to crowd into the concession, eager to celebrate my arrival.

Late that night when everyone was in bed I went and sat beside my father under the veranda of his hut. The director had told me he had to have my father's formal consent before he could to anything, and that it should reach him with as little delay as possible.

"Father," I said, "when the director asked me if I would like to go to France I said yes."

"Ah! You've already accepted."

"I couldn't help saying yes. I didn't think what I was saying at the time, or what you and my mother would think."

"Do you really want to go?"

"Yes. Uncle Mamadou says it's a unique opportunity."

"You could have gone to Dakar. Your uncle went to Dakar."

"It wouldn't be the same thing."

"No, it wouldn't. But how are we going to break the news to your mother?"

"Then you agree I should go?"

"Yes . . . Yes, I'm willing. For your sake. For your own good."

And he was silent a while.

"It's something I've often thought about," he said. "I've thought about it night and day. I knew quite well that eventually you would leave us. I knew it the very first time you set foot in school. I watched you studying with such eagerness, such passionate eagerness! . . . Yes, since that day I have known how it would be. And gradually I resigned myself to it."

"Father!"

"Each one follows his own destiny, my son. Men cannot change what is decreed. Your uncles too have had an education. As for me—but I've already told you; remember what I said when you went away to Conakry—I hadn't the opportunities they had, let alone yours. This opportunity is within your reach. You must seize it. You've already seized one; seize this one too; make sure of it. There are still so many things to be done in our land. . . . Yes, I want you to go to France. I want that now, just as much as you do. Soon we'll be needing men like you here. . . . May you not be gone too long!"

We sat under the veranda for a long time without saying anything, looking out into the night. Then suddenly my father said in a broken voice, "Promise me that you will come back."

"I will come back."

"Those distant lands . . ." he whispered slowly.

He left the phrase unfinished and continued to stare into the darkness. I could see him by the light of the storm lantern, staring as if at a fixed point and frowning as if he were dissatisfied at what he saw.

"What are you looking at?" I asked.

"Take care never to deceive anyone," he said. "Be upright in thought and deed. And God will be with you."

Then he made what seemed a gesture of despair and turned his eyes away from the darkness.

The next day I wrote the director that my father had given his permission. And I began to dream about Paris. I had heard about Paris for so long! Then my thoughts returned abruptly to my mother.

"Have you told her yet?" I asked.

"No. We'll go together."

"You wouldn't like to tell her yourself?"

"By myself? No, my son. Believe me, even if we both go we'll be outnumbered."

We went to look for her. We found her crushing millet for the evening meal. My father stood watching the pestle falling in the mortar. He scarcely knew where to begin. The decision he had had to make would hurt my mother, and his own heart was heavy. He stood there watching the pestle and saying nothing. I dared not lift my eyes. But she was not long in guessing what was up. She had only to look at us to understand everything or almost everything.

"What do you want?" she asked. "Can't you see I'm busy?"

And she began pounding faster and faster.

"Don't go so fast," my father said. "You'll wear yourself out."

"Are you teaching me how to pound millet?" she asked.

Then all of a sudden she went on angrily, "If it's about the boy's going to France you can save your breath. He's not going!"

"That's just it," said my father. "You don't know what you're talking about. You don't realize what such an opportunity means to him."

"I don't want to know."

Suddenly she dropped the pestle and took a few steps toward us.

"Am I never to have peace? Yesterday it was the school in Conakry; today it's the school in France; tomorrow . . . what will it be tomorrow? Every day there's some mad scheme to take my son away from me! . . . Have you already forgotten how sick he was in Conakry? But that's not enough for you. Now you want to send him to France! Are you crazy? Or do you want to drive me out of my mind? I'll certainly end up raving mad. . . . And as for you," she cried, turning to me, "you are nothing but an ungrateful son. Any excuse is good enough for you to run away from your mother. But this time it won't be as *you* want. You'll stay right here. Your place is here. . . . What *are* they thinking about at the school? Do they imagine I'm going to live my whole life apart from my son? Die with him far away? Have they no mothers, those people? They can't have. They wouldn't have gone so far away from home if they had."

She lifted up her eyes to the sky and addressed the heavens, "He's been away from me so many years already! And now they want to take him away to their own land! . . ."

Then she lowered her gaze and looked at my father again. "Would you let them do that? Have you no heart?"

"Woman! Woman! Don't you know it's for his own good?"

"His own good? The best thing for him is to stay here with us. Hasn't he learned enough already?"

"Mother," I began.

But she turned on me violently, "You be quiet! You're still just a little boy, a nobody. What do you want to go so far away for? Do you have any idea how people live out there? . . . No, you don't know anything about it. And tell me this, who's going to look after you? Who's going to mend your clothes? Who'll cook for you?"

"Come, come," said my father. "Be reasonable. The white men don't die of hunger."

"So you haven't noticed, you poor crazy thing, you haven't even noticed that they don't eat the way we do. The child will fall sick; that's what will happen. And then what will I do? What will become of me? Oh! I had a son once, but now I have none!"

I went up to her and took her in my arms.

"Get away from me!" she shouted. "You're no son of mine!"

But she did not push me away. She was weeping and she held me close.

"You won't leave me alone, will you? Tell me you won't leave me all alone."

But now she knew that I would go away and that she could not stop me, that nothing could stop me. Perhaps she had known from the first. Yes, she must have guessed that this was a matter where there were wheels within wheels. They had taken me from the school in Kouroussa to

Conakry and finally to France. All the time she had been talking and fighting against them, she must have been watching the wheels going round and round: first this wheel, then that, and then a third and greater wheel, then still more, many more, perhaps, which no one could see. And how could they be stopped? We could only watch them turning and turning, the wheels of destiny turning and turning. My destiny was to go away from home. And my mother began to turn her anger on those who, she thought, were taking me away from her. But by now her anger was futile: "Those people are never satisfied. They want to have every-thing. As soon as they set eyes on something they want it for themselves."

"You shouldn't malign them," I replied.

"No," she said bitterly. "I shall not malign them."

Finally her anger and her rage were spent. She laid her head on my shoulder and wept loudly. My father had crept away. I held her close, I dried her tears, I said . . . what did I say to her? Everything and anything that came into my head but nothing of any importance. I don't think she understood a word. All she was aware of was the sound of my voice. That was enough. Her sobs gradually became quieter and less frequent. . . .

That was how my departure was arranged. And so one day I took a plane for France. Oh! it was a terrible parting! I do not like to think of it. I can still hear my mother wailing. I still see my father, un-able to hide his tears. I can still see my sisters, my brothers. . . . No, I do not like to remember that parting. It was as if I were being torn apart.

Look what they done to my song

Look what they done to my song, Ma.
Look what they done to my song.
Well, it's the only thing that I could do
    half right,
And it's turnin' out all wrong, Ma.
Look what they done to my song....

I wish I could find a good book to live in
Wish I could find a good book
Well, if I could find a real good book
I'd never have to come out and look
At what they done to my song.

From "What Have They Done to My Song, Ma"
by Melanie Safka (U.S.A.).

Shades of Gray

BARRY MANN and CYNTHIA WEIL

When the world and I were young just yesterday
Life was such a simple game a child could play
It was easy then to tell right from wrong
Easy then to tell weak from strong
When a man should stand and fight
Or just go along

But today there is no day or night
Today there is no dark or light
Today there is no black or white
Only shades of gray

I remember when the answers seemed so clear
We had never lived with doubt or tasted fear
It was easy then to tell truth from lies
Selling out from compromise
Whom to love and whom to hate
The foolish from the wise

But today there is no day or night
Today there is no dark or light
Today there is no black or white
Only shades of gray

It was easy then to know what was fair
What to keep and what to share
How much to protect your heart
And how much to care

But today there is no day or night
Today there is no dark or light
Today there is no black or white
Only shades of gray

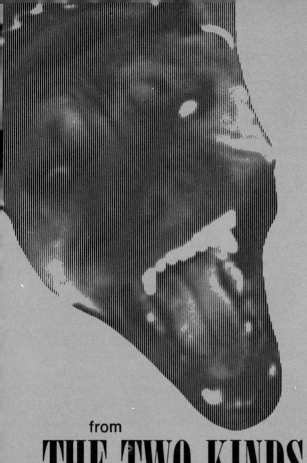

from
THE TWO KINDS OF TRUTH

PYOTR ZAMOYSKI

"He'll give; Uncle Ossip will," Mom said. "They've lots of grain, all shelves full."

Did Mother really believe when she said that Uncle Ossip won't refuse? She probably didn't because her face was worried and her eyes were scared. There were nine mouths to feed in our family and they'd given us soil for one and one-half souls. Only my dad had the right to soil and our oldest brother, now in the army. My dad was one soul and the soldier boy one-half; we kids didn't count—we were "soulless" they said. That had been the law, and after the law was made there was no more soil to share out. . . .

Though we weren't looking at the street any more we knew by the passing shadow that Dad was home. We could see him now standing at the door of our cottage. He groaned for a while, fumbling and knocking at something, then began to scrape, as if groping for the cramp. There was a jerk, and then . . . the door opened slowly, slowly.

Dad didn't look at us, at our worried faces. He lazily laid the empty bag on the Dutch stove we had, rubbed his hands as if they had been frozen, and only then did he give us a glance—sort of begging and scared too. It seemed as if Dad was afraid of us, his own kids. He was afraid and felt guilty. None of us said anything, and there was silence for a long time which Dad seemed to find harder and harder to stand. We all knew that Mom would be first to speak up. She lifted her tearful face, chewed for a while on her dried-up lips and began to shake her head.

"You're nothing but a piece of clay," she said bitterly to Dad. Mom was speaking very softly but we all heard her . . . he too. "You're a good-for-nothing goofy nincompoop unfit even to be shot by a good cannon. Why don't we get rid of you before you tire us all out to death?" Mom kept scolding Dad and us.

Dad didn't say anything; he knew that if he said something they might end fighting with the wooden poker. So he just shook his head and whispered, "Oh, you stupid nag, you nag!"

When Mom finished scolding she got up from the bench, made a step toward the stove and snatched the bag. Giving Dad a look that almost made him stagger, she slammed the door and left.

I ran after and caught up with her at the pantry shed. "Mommy, where're you going?" I asked.

She stopped and stared at me. Then she bent down as if looking for a stick but I didn't wait. "You miserable brat," I heard her scream. "Go home before I make a short end of you."

I ran back. I knew where she was going anyhow—to the Karpukhins. The Karpukhins were richer than the Glazovs but more stingy. Dad wouldn't even try there; only Mom had a chance. Mom knew how to go about these things; she'd not crawl or bow as Dad did. No, she'd pretend to laugh, joke, and wouldn't ask for anything at first. Only later she'd say, as if it suddenly came to her, "Heck, I just thought of something. I'd started on the dough and found I haven't got enough flour. Could you help me out with a measure until tomorrow?"

The Karpukhins knew only too well that "tomorrow" meant until fall. Still only rarely did they refuse Mom. True, they'd first make fun out of Dad, out of our whole household, our misery, and then they'd either give right away or promise to.

I waited until I saw her come out of the Karpukhins' porch. I knew from her face that she got it.

"Mom?" I asked softly, "are we going to get it?"

"We are," she said.

"When?"

"Don't be nosy," she snapped. "They're takin' a lorry to the mill tomorrow, an' after they come back they'll give us two measures till New Moon."

I ran inside. When Mom came in, everybody knew by her face that we were going to have bread. Even Dad cheered up though he asked no questions.

II

Lukashka was from Kochki, not far from here; he was living in our village now, working for the rich farmer Damyotka. Several years older than me, Lukashka was a strong lad and a good worker. He had only one good eye, though; the other a shepherd had spattered out with a whip.

Lukashka had been telling me interesting things and giving me books to read. Whenever I had a chance to crawl up into the attic, I'd sit down at the chimney where there was a hole in the roof and read. Mom couldn't find me there, no matter how hard she looked. I knew if she ever found me there she would take my book away and tear it to pieces.

"Get on the cart," Lukashka invited me.

I jumped up. I looked at the two-share plow dragging behind us on its wheels, then watched Lukashka's huge dog Kaukas, running ahead of the cart. Kaukas was big and yellow, came out on top in most dogfights. And Lukashka loved to see dogs fight; he'd seem to change when he sicked them. "Sick'em Kaukas!" he'd yell, and Kaukas'd throw himself at his enemy from a running jump.

We barely managed to get by two boundary stones from the meadow when a two-horse cart showed up on the road crossing. It was driven by Pavel, one of Karpukhin's married sons. Pavel was older than Lukashka but he always liked to ride out into the fields with *his* dog, the huge Polkan. He too loved to see dogs fight. His Polkan had already been in many fights with Lukashka's Kaukas; sometimes one, sometimes the other dog won.

"Hello there, Lukashka," Pavel shouted.

"Hello there, Pavel. Opening the fall tilling?"

The dogs were already snarling at each other. Pavel's eyes began to flash. "Look at them," he shouted with joy.

"They know their business," Lukashka said.

"Shall we sick'em, what d'ya say?" Pavel asked.

"Why not?"

They stopped their horses and jumped off the carts. "Go get'im, Polkan!" Pavel shouted.

"Take'm, Kaukas!" Lukashka yelled.

The dogs seemed to be waiting just for that; they jumped at each other, turned over a few times, and bunched in a cloud of dust. Each dog had his own way of fighting; Polkan tried to grab his enemy's throat. Kaukas aimed for the upper lip. The winner would usually be the dog that made the first grab.

This time Kaukas had goofed. Almost at once Polkan had his throat. Whooping happily, Pavel kept running around the dogs, baiting Polkan, "Get'im!"

Lukashka, too, ran around, yelling, "Take'm, Kaukas! Take'm!"

The dogs whirled, uprooting grass and crushing somebody's millet. Kaukas was pressed to the ground, his throat in Polkan's teeth. He had stopped growling, whined for a while, then began to groan hoarsely.

I sat on the cart, trembling from fright and watching little rivers of sweat flowing down Lukashka's face. Kids had come hurrying down from the meadow, and they too, like Pavel and Lukashka, started running around the dogs, whistling and yowling.

Kaukas was quiet and all bloody as Polkan was sitting on top of him, biting his throat. "Lukashka," I yelled out. "*Do* something, he'll chew Kaukas to death."

Lukashka had seen that. He made up his mind to do the last thing he'd have wanted to. Running up to the dogs, he kicked Kaukas as hard as he could. "S-sick 'im," he shouted. "S-sick 'im!"

Kaukas shot up like a flash of lightning. Before I could blink an eye he was on top of Polkan, clamping him with his paws and sinking his teeth in his enemy's upper jaw. There was Polkan's scared yap, as Kaukas tossed him up and threw him against the plow, and then clamped him again with his paws, tearing at his side and throwing off bloody clumps of hair.

Pavel became pale and began darting around the wrestling dogs. "Get'im," he kept yelling, kicking Polkan, but Polkan couldn't tear himself away from Kaukas's teeth. Then Pavel grabbed a stick and began to hit Kaukas, which was something a dog baiter wasn't supposed to do, because when the owners wanted to separate the dogs they had to beat their own.

"Mister Pavel," Lukashka shouted, "Why're you hitting *my* dog?"

"Shut up," Pavel shouted back, hitting Kaukas harder and harder.

"Stop hitting my dog," Lukashka screamed, trying to take away the stick from Pavel. But Pavel swung around and hit Lukashka on the face with it. Lukashka's nose began to bleed. He wanted to pull the stick out of Pavel's hand and hit him back with it, but Pavel grabbed his hand and struck him a few more times on the face.

"Mister Pavel," Lukashka began to cry. "Why're you hitting me?" He turned around to the kids who had been watching. "You'll witness that he hit me," he said. "I'm going to complain to the village constable."

Pavel started to cow the kids. "Have you seen me hitting him?" he asked. "You haven't, right?"

The kids were scared. "No, we haven't!" they said running away.

"You little cowards," Lukashka shouted angrily, smearing the blood over his face. "You're afraid to testify against a rich man, you! I don't care, I've a witness anyway."

"And who's that?" Pavel sneered.

"Him," Lukashka pointed at me.

Pavel looked at me calmly. "Will you witness?" he asked.

"I will," I answered in a voice trembling from fear and anger.

"Go on," Pavel shouted. "Go on. What're you going to tell the constable?"

"I'll tell him that you hit Lukashka."

"Go on, tell him," Pavel dared. "Go on, tell him, and tomorrow your mother's going to come to us for flour."

I turned away from Pavel, not saying anything, Lukashka was silent too. The dogs had stopped fighting; tired and bleeding they lay against each other, licking their wounds. Lukashka jerked the reins of his horse. Pavel swerved to the boundary ridge. The dogs rose and followed their masters; I got off the cart and began walking home.

The rest of the day my ears were ringing with Pavel's words: "Go on, tell him, and tomorrow your mother's going to come to us for flour!"

III

I didn't tell Mother anything. At night I dreamt of nothing but dogs. I lost my breath from fear. I began to roll over and over, and then . . . I woke up. Mother stood beside me, shaking my shoulder. "Go on, hurry to the constable," I heard her whisper. "The foreman's here waiting for you."

Mother called me out into the porch. She looked around to make sure that the door was tightly shut behind and told me in an angry, clipped whisper, "Don't you get it into your head to finger Mr. Pavel.

You've seen nothing, hear? What's that one-eyed Lukashka to you any-way? Today he's a sore mug; tomorrow he'll forget all about it. But if the Karpukhins refuse us flour, we croak from hunger. Hear?"

I remembered yesterday's incident very clearly. I was so scared that a chill hit me on the spine. "Mom," I said, "I'm going to tell only the truth."

"Which truth?" she asked, drawing her face close to mine.

"That Mister Pavel hit Lukashka."

Mother's fist came near my nose. "You daresn't. I'll give you the licking of your life, hear? Pavel's never laid a hand on Lukashka. Never, you hear? And don't you dare lie to the constable; you sing the truth or else."

"I'll tell the truth," I promised.

"Which one?" Mother asked again.

I had no time to answer. Out came the foreman and led me off to the Hall, the villagers' meeting place. When we walked out into the street, kids began to follow us. Mother, too, followed all the time looking around herself like a thief. . . .

The Hall was full. The foreman nudged me ahead through the crowd, toward the constable sitting behind a desk. "Here's your chief witness," he said, seeming to be talking to the constable and the folks at the same time.

The constable adjusted the saber hanging at his side and set back the blue-ribboned cap to the back of his head. Then he wrinkled his brow and looked at me sternly. Pavel, sitting next to him, smiled at me gaily and stroked his mustache. "Your Excellency, ask Vasya here, and he'll tell you that it wasn't me that hit One-Eye there," Pavel said, nodding toward Lukashka sitting glumly a little farther away in the corner. "Dogs we sicked, true—but hit him? I never laid a hand on the lad. I'd never smear up a boy's mug like that, no sir!"

Lukashka stared at the ceiling. His face was swollen; there were black welts round his eyes. The constable screwed up his eyes and although I stood almost next to the desk, he said to me, "You boy, will you come a little closer."

I made a step closer; my knees buckled under me.

"Were you in the fields with Lukyan at lunchtime yesterday?" the constable asked.

"I was," I said.

"Who else was there?"

"Mister Pavel here. . . ."

"And what were you doing there?"

"Sicking dogs," I said.

"Then what?"

"Then?" I repeated and looked back for some reason. I saw my mother; she began to blink her eyes and shake her head so hard that I forgot what I'd wanted to say.

"Well, come on, talk," the constable insisted.

"Then . . ." I began, stepping from foot to foot. "Then . . . Then . . ." No words came out. When I had pointed at Mr. Pavel, I saw him draw his brows together so hard and toss his head so fiercely that I'd forgot the tongue in my mouth. The folks behind began to make loud noises. "Talk, talk," they asked me.

"Quiet," the constable roared. "Then what?" he turned to me again. "Tell the truth, did Pavel Karpukhin hit Lukyan, or was it Lukyan himself that fell and hit his head against the plow? You tell the truth, boy!"

"Constable, sir," Lukashka shouted angrily, jumping up from the bench, "this is not the way to make an inquest."

"Don't you try to teach me," the constable reddened on the face. "You know what you may get for this?"

"I'm not trying to teach you, sir," Lukashka answered. "I'm only trying to say you shouldn't scare the boy. Vasya," Lukashka turned to me, "tell the truth, Vasya. How it was, what you saw—don't be afraid; nothing'll happen to you if you tell the truth."

"Sure," Pavel boomed. "Nothing'll happen. . . ."

"Nothing'll happen if you tell the truth," I heard people buzzing behind me. "He, our little Vasya'll never tell a lie," I heard my mother's voice trembling with tears. "He always tells the truth."

"Come on, talk," the constable kept insisting while at the same time scribbling something on a piece of paper.

They were asking me to tell them the truth and I didn't know which truth to tell them—the real truth, that Pavel had given Lukashka a beating? Whenever I opened my mouth to say it, my eyes met with Mr. Pavel's frowning face and I heard those words ringing in my ears: Go on, tell, and your mother'll come tomorrow for flour. Should I tell them that Lukashka fell and hit himself on the plow? Lukashka's reproachful eyes, his beat-up face met my eyes and made me feel ashamed of myself. Which kind of truth was the truer, I asked myself?

"Come on, talk," I heard Mr. Pavel chime in. "They haven't hung anyone for tellin' the truth."

It was hard for me, a twelve-year-old boy, to decide which kind of truth to tell; the Lukashka kind with its beat-up face, or the Pavel kind that looked like two measures of flour? I remembered how we had been waiting yesterday for our father to come back from the Glazovs; how Mom scolded and how she went to the Karpukhins . . . I remembered it and not knowing myself I let the words come out, "Mr. Pavel hadn't hit Lukashka; he fell and cut himself on the plow. . . ."

I said it and broke out in tears. I cried because I thought it wasn't me that had spoken but some other boy. I heard a sigh of relief, probably my mother's, and I heard Pavel's gay voice, "I've been tellin' you the kid'll tell the truth." Then, as if in a dream, I heard my mother's voice, "My boy's always been so so much for the truth always. . . ."

From all these words, Mr. Pavel's, my Mom's, the floor seemed to sway under me. I thought I was falling, and my face began to burn, and my heart was ready to jump out, and my knees began to buckle. I saw the constable writing down something; then I heard him say, "So in other words, it wasn't he who hit him."

What else I might have said I don't know, were it not that I heard Lukashka—One-Eye, as they call him. There was the poor orphan whom I loved for the books that he had given me and for so many other things. "Ey, you, you Vasya . . ." I heard his reproachful sigh.

These words made me ache. I quickly turned around, caught a glimpse of my mother's happy smile, of Pavel's happy face, of those wondering villagers and suddenly, surprising everybody in the room, I began to shout out in anger. "No, no, Mr. Pavel *did* hit Lukashka. He hit him and hit him. He gave'm a bloody nose and all that. He pushed him down and hit him again. It was him, Mr. Pavel. An' I don't want your flour, you can keep it. I don't want it, I don't. . . ."

Somebody else had begun to shout but I saw nothing until somebody grabbed my hand and pulled me. I felt a burning on my cheek—my mother was slapping me. She had dragged me out onto the street; her face was twisted from hateful fear and anger; she kept slapping me on the face and screaming, "Will you tell the truth, will you, will you. . . ."

I rocked from side to side, repeating like a dummy, "I will, I will, I will . . ."

Mother kept hitting and hitting me. But the more she slapped, the more stubborn and contrary I'd become. And then I caught her finger with my teeth and bit. Mother ouched and let go of me. I broke away and began to run. I ran through yards, through fields and dove into the hemp.

IV

I sneaked into my favorite hut, scrambled onto an old pile of chaff and took out the last piece of bread from my pocket. I had deliberately saved it. A while later, when it became quite dark I heard fast steps outside. My heart jumped at the familiar voice, "Where could that devil's brood be? Just let me get my hands on him!"

She was still looking for me! I was afraid Mom might take a peek inside where she had surprised me already with a book in my hands. I got out through a hole on the side, crawled on the ground, until I reached the threshing floor. Then I began to run. I ran along field boundaries, then turned onto the street. The dark night made my fears grow and grow. I walked and walked, not knowing where to stop. Lukashka! Why not go to him? I thought.

Lukashka always slept in his master's barn. "This is my nest," he'd tell me. I softly opened the door and took a peek. He was still awake. "Is it you, Vasya?" he asked.

"It's me," I said. "What're you doing?"

"Thinking. Can't sleep. Come up here, Vasya. Where've you been?"

"Everywhere." We were silent for a while.

"You mean you weren't home?" he asked me.

"I musn't go home. Mom'll beat me up."

"It's because of the truth," he said.

"The truth! Eh, you're like all the others," I waved my hand. "Everybody says you've got to tell the truth and nothing'll come to you. Truth doesn't burn, doesn't sting, but . . ."

"But it depends which kind of truth," Lukashka laughed. "There're two, you know. One's poor, carries a bag; the other's rich, has a trunk. If you tell the first one, you get it with a stick over your paws; if you tell the other one, you get bread into them."

I thought of the flour and the beating mother gave me. "You're so right," I said sadly. "Now there'll be no flour for us; the bin in the pantry shed'll stay empty and we'll croak from hunger."

"Uh, don't worry," Lukashka muttered. He might have been talking to me or to himself.

He woke me up early next morning. "Go on home now, Vasya," he told me. "I've got to go out tilling."

I rubbed my eyes and scrambled down from his "nest." I went toward home but then stopped behind the corner of our cottage to watch. Mother was driving the sheep out to pasture—her face was smeared, tearful. I thought she was probably awake most of the night, crying, maybe worrying about me, maybe about the flour.

Pavel's wife had driven the cows out of the Karpukhin yard. Seeing Mother, she stopped and rocked her heavy, pregnant belly. "Ari-ii-nushka," she chanted loud'n clear for the whole street to hear. "You awlready t'come for the flour? Your bag wide'n roo-oo-my? Ey you miserable beggar woman, you moo-oo-cher. Ever thought of raisin' your own bread, you good-f'nothin baa-aggars?"

My mother, the champion name-caller and quarreler, didn't answer a word. She smirked sheepishly and hurried back home. But then, I don't know whether I gave myself away by leaning out too far, or Mom just happened to take a glimpse in my direction; there she stopped and stared at me. I remained like chained to the ground as she slowly moved toward me, swinging that stick she used to drive out the sheep.

"Wa-al," she finally shouted. "Get in already, get in. Where've you been? What do you care that your mother's worryin' to death about you? Wa-al, get in, get in. Hey," she shouted at Dad, "come here and help me catch this brat so I can lay my hands on him."

Happen what may, I decided, I'm going to walk up to her myself. "Go on, hit me Mom," I dared. "Kill me. I don't care. I'm a goner anyway."

My words might have stunned her. It might have been she was glad inside that I'd come back. She raised her stick as if to hit me, but instead, took a hold of my hair and waved a bandaged finger in front of my nose. "Look what you've done, look wha . . ." Mom groaned heavily and began to cry before she finished the sentence.

I pushed my head into her apron. "Mommy, Mommy," I pleaded. "I'd rather have you beat me up than hear you cry. Mommy, I'm sorry I wore you out; please beat me up an' you'll feel better. You will. . . ."

She stopped crying and threw away the stick. Her hand moved affectionately over my head, then gave me a light tap on the shoulder. "Go inside," she said softly. "You must be hungry."

I went inside with her following. She set a pot full of potatoes in front of me on the table. "Because of you, you little imp, they gave us no flour," she growled, without looking at me. "An' two full lorries they ground up yesterday. . . ." While my little sister and I ate potatoes, Mom went out to the pantry shed to bring me a slice of bread from the last loaf we had been eating a whole week already. She came back a few minutes later, a mixture of fright and joy on her face. She winked at Dad who was gulping the potato water. "Father," she whispered at him, "come out with me, quick."

"Why?" he asked guiltily.

"Where did you scrounge up the flour?" she asked.

"What flour?" Dad looked at her, then at us in amazement.

"Come take a look at the pantry," she pointed her head.

He got up, wiping his hands on his pants. We went out—Mom leading, me right behind her, and the rest of us following. She led us to the bin in the pantry. "There," she pointed.

Dad rubbed his eyes and bent over. "My Lord," he exclaimed, taking a handful of flour, "what's this? Where did you hustle it up, Mother?"

"That's what I'm askin' you," she replied. "Where did you get it?"

"Don't know anything, Mother. Don't know a thing, so help me." Dad kept shaking his head.

He and Mother and all of us stood there over the bin, basking our eyes in about three measures of beautiful flour. Where did it come from? we asked ourselves. I was getting dizzy from trying to think. Where did it come from? I asked myself time and time again. Then a thought struck me. This thought made me tremble, and in my trembling I hadn't realized that I said aloud, "You won't croak from hunger!"

"What did you say?" Mother asked.

"You won't croak," I repeated in a clear voice; then looking around as if to tell a secret, I began to explain in a whisper, "That's Lukashka's flour. . . . Last night . . ."

Dad sighed and mumbled. Mom bent over the bin and cried. Her tears fell into the flour and made a few tiny clumps.

Translated by Selig O. Wassner

Czechoslovakia—The Two Kinds of Truth

TUESDAY SIESTA

GABRIEL GARCIA-MARQUEZ

The train emerged from the quivering tunnel of sandy rocks, began to cross the symmetrical, interminable banana plantations, and the air became humid and they couldn't feel the sea breeze anymore. A stifling blast of smoke came in the car window. On the narrow road parallel to the railway there were oxcarts loaded with green bunches of

130

bananas. Beyond the road, in odd, uncultivated spaces, there were offices with electric fans, red brick buildings, and residences with chairs and little white tables on the terraces among dusty palm trees and rose-bushes. It was eleven in the morning, and the heat had not yet begun.

"You'd better close the window," the woman said. "Your hair will get full of soot."

The girl tried to, but the shade wouldn't move because of the rust.

They were the only passengers in the lone third-class car. Since the smoke of the locomotive kept coming through the window, the girl left her seat and put down the only things they had with them: a plastic sack with some things to eat and a bouquet of flowers wrapped in newspaper. She sat on the opposite seat, away from the window, facing her mother. They were both in severe and poor mourning clothes.

The girl was twelve years old, and it was the first time she'd ever been on a train. The woman seemed too old to be her mother, because of the blue veins on her eyelids and her small, soft, and shapeless body, in a dress cut like a cassock. She was riding with her spinal column braced firmly against the back of the seat, and held a peeling patent-leather portfolio in her lap with both hands. She bore the conscientious serenity of someone accustomed to poverty.

By twelve the heat had begun. The train stopped for ten minutes to take on water at a station where there was no town. Outside, in the mysterious silence of the plantations, the shadows seemed clean. But the still air inside the car smelled like untanned leather. The train did not pick up speed. It stopped at two identical towns with wooden houses painted bright colors. The woman's head nodded and she sank into sleep. The girl took off her shoes. Then she went to the washroom to put the bouquet of flowers in some water.

When she came back to her seat, her mother was waiting to eat. She gave her a piece of cheese, half a cornmeal pancake, and a cookie, and took an equal portion out of the plastic sack for herself. While they ate, the train crossed an iron bridge very slowly and passed a town just like the ones before, except that in this one there was a crowd in the plaza. A band was playing a lively tune under the oppressive sun. At the other side of town the plantations ended in a plain which was cracked from the drought.

The woman stopped eating.

"Put on your shoes," she said.

The girl looked outside. She saw nothing but the deserted plain, where the train began to pick up speed again, but she put the last piece of cookie into the sack and quickly put on her shoes. The woman gave her a comb.

"Comb your hair," she said.

The train whistle began to blow while the girl was combing her hair.

The woman dried the sweat from her neck and wiped the oil from her face with her fingers. When the girl stopped combing, the train was passing the outlying houses of a town larger but sadder than the earlier ones.

"If you feel like doing anything, do it now," said the woman. "Later, don't take a drink anywhere even if you're dying of thirst. Above all, no crying."

The girl nodded her head. A dry, burning wind came in the window, together with the locomotive's whistle and the clatter of the old cars. The woman wrapped up the pancake with the rest of the food and put it in the portfolio. For a moment a complete picture of the town, on that bright August Tuesday, shone in the window. The girl wrapped the flowers in the soaking-wet newspapers, moved a little farther away from the window, and stared at her mother. She received a pleasant expression in return. The train began to whistle and slowed down. A moment later it stopped.

There was no one at the station. On the other side of the street, on the sidewalk shaded by the almond trees, only the pool hall was open. The town was floating in the heat. The woman and the girl got off the train and crossed the abandoned station—the tiles split apart by the grass growing up between—and the street to the shady sidewalk.

It was almost two. At that hour, weighted down by drowsiness, the town was taking a siesta. The stores, the town offices, the public school were closed at eleven, and didn't reopen until a little before four, when the train went back. Only the hotel across from the station, with its bar and pool hall, and the telegraph office at one side of the plaza stayed open. The houses, most of them built on the banana company's model, had their doors locked from inside and their blinds drawn. In some of them it was so hot that the residents ate lunch in the patio. Others leaned a chair against the wall, in the shade of the almond trees, and took their siesta right out in the street.

Keeping to the protective shade of the almond trees, the woman and the girl entered the town without disturbing the siesta. They went directly to the priest's house. The woman scratched the metal grating on the door with her fingernail, waited a moment, and scratched again. An electric fan was humming inside. They did not hear the steps. They hardly heard the slight creaking of a door, and immediately a cautious voice, right next to the metal grating: "Who is it?" The woman tried to see through the grating.

"I need the Father," she said.

"He's sleeping now."

"It's an emergency," the woman insisted.

Her voice showed a calm determination.

The door was opened a little way, noiselessly, and a plump, older woman appeared, with very pale skin and hair the color of iron. Her eyes seemed too small behind her thick eyeglasses.

"Come in," she said, and opened the door all the way.

They entered a room permeated with an old smell of flowers. The woman of the house led them to a wooden bench and signaled them to sit down. The girl did so, but her mother remained standing, absent-mindedly, with both hands clutching the portfolio. No noise could be heard above the electric fan.

The woman of the house reappeared at the door at the far end of the room. "He says you should come back after three," she said in a very low voice. "He just lay down five minutes ago."

"The train leaves at three-thirty," said the woman.

It was a brief and self-assured reply, but her voice remained pleasant, full of undertones. The woman of the house smiled for the first time.

"All right," she said.

When the far door closed again, the woman sat down next to her daughter. The narrow waiting room was poor, neat, and clean. On the other side of the wooden railing which divided the room, there was a worktable, a plain one with an oilcloth cover, and on top of the table a primitive typewriter next to a vase of flowers. The parish records were beyond. You could see that it was an office kept in order by a spinster.

The far door opened and this time the priest appeared, cleaning his glasses with a handkerchief. Only when he put them on was it evident that he was the brother of the woman who had opened the door.

"How can I help you?" he asked.

"The keys to the cemetery," said the woman.

The girl was seated with the flowers in her lap and her feet crossed under the bench. The priest looked at her, then looked at the woman, and then through the wire mesh of the window at the bright, cloudless sky.

"In this heat," he said. "You could have waited until the sun went down."

The woman moved her head silently. The priest crossed to the other side of the railing, took out of the cabinet a notebook covered in oil-cloth, a wooden penholder, and an inkwell, and sat down at the table. There was more than enough hair on his hands to account for what was missing on his head.

"Which grave are you going to visit?" he asked.

"Carlos Centeno's," said the woman.

"Who?"

"Carlos Centeno," the woman repeated.

The priest still did not understand.

"He's the thief who was killed here last week," said the woman in the same tone of voice. "I am his mother."

The priest scrutinized her. She stared at him with quiet self-control, and the Father blushed. He lowered his head and began to write. As he filled the page, he asked the woman to identify herself, and she replied unhesitatingly, with precise details, as if she were reading them. The Father began to sweat. The girl unhooked the buckle of her left shoe, slipped her heel out of it, and rested it on the bench rail. She did the same with the right one.

It had all started the Monday of the previous week, at three in the morning, a few blocks from there. Rebecca, a lonely widow who lived in a house full of odds and ends, heard above the sound of the drizzling rain someone trying to force the front door from outside. She got up, rummaged around in her closet for an ancient revolver that no one had fired since the days of Colonel Aureliano Buendia, and went into the living room without turning on the lights. Orienting herself not so much by the noise at the lock as by a terror developed in her by twenty-eight years of loneliness, she fixed in her imagination not only the spot where the door was but also the exact height of the lock. She clutched the weapon with both hands, closed her eyes, and squeezed the trigger. It was the first time in her life that she had fired a gun. Immediately after the explosion, she could hear nothing except the murmur of the drizzle on the galvanized roof. Then she heard a little metallic bump on the cement porch, and a very low voice, pleasant but terribly exhausted: "Ah, Mother." The man they found dead in front of the house in the morning, his nose blown to bits, wore a flannel shirt with colored stripes, everyday pants with a rope for a belt, and was barefoot. No one in town knew him.

"So his name was Carlos Centeno," murmured the Father when he finished writing.

"Centeno Ayala," said the woman. "He was my only boy."

The priest went back to the cabinet. Two big rusty keys hung on the inside of the door; the girl imagined, as her mother had when she was a girl and as the priest himself must have imagined at some time, that they were Saint Peter's keys. He took them down, put them on the open notebook on the railing, and pointed with his forefinger to a place on the page he had just written, looking at the woman.

"Sign here."

The woman scribbled her name, holding the portfolio under her arm. The girl picked up the flowers, came to the railing shuffling her feet, and watched her mother attentively.

The priest sighed.

"Didn't you ever try to get him on the right track?"

The woman answered when she finished signing.

"He was a very good man."

The priest looked first at the woman and then at the girl, and realized with a kind of pious amazement that they were not about to cry. The woman continued in the same tone:

"I told him never to steal anything that anyone needed to eat, and he minded me. On the other hand, before, when he used to box, he used to spend three days in bed, exhausted from being punched."

"All his teeth had to be pulled out," interrupted the girl.

"That's right," the woman agreed. "Every mouthful I ate those days tasted of the beatings my son got on Saturday nights."

"God's will is inscrutable," said the Father.

But he said it without much conviction, partly because experience had made him a little skeptical and partly because of the heat. He suggested that they cover their heads to guard against sunstroke. Yawning, and now almost completely asleep, he gave them instructions about how to find Carlos Centeno's grave. When they came back, they didn't have to knock. They should put the key under the door; and in the same place, if they could, they should put an offering for the Church. The woman listened to his directions with great attention, but thanked him without smiling.

The Father had noticed that there was someone looking inside, his nose pressed against the metal grating, even before he opened the door to the street. Outside was a group of children. When the door was opened wide, the children scattered. Ordinarily, at that hour there was no one in the street. Now there were not only children. There were groups of people under the almond trees. The Father scanned the street swimming in the heat and then he understood. Softly, he closed the door again.

"Wait a moment," he said without looking at the woman.

His sister appeared at the far door with a black jacket over her nightshirt and her hair down over her shoulders. She looked silently at the Father.

"What was it?" he asked.

"The people have noticed," murmured his sister.

"You'd better go out by the door to the patio," said the Father.

"It's the same there," said his sister. "Everybody is at the windows."

The woman seemed not to have understood until then. She tried to look into the street through the metal grating. Then she took the bouquet of flowers from the girl and began to move toward the door. The girl followed her.

"Wait until the sun goes down," said the Father.

"You'll melt," said his sister, motionless at the back of the room. "Wait and I'll lend you a parasol."

"Thank you," replied the woman. "We're all right this way."

She took the girl by the hand and went into the street.

Translated by J. S. Bernstein

from

The Wretched of the Earth

FRANTZ FANON

Case Number 1 *While under hospital treatment, a European policeman in a depressed state meets one of his victims, an Algerian patriot who is suffering from stupor.*

A ____, twenty-eight years old, no children. . . . We learned that for several years both he and his wife underwent treatment, unfortunately with no success, in order to have children. He was sent to us by his superiors because he had behavior disturbances.

Immediate contact seemed fairly good. The patient spoke to us spontaneously about his difficulties. Satisfactory relations with his wife and parents-in-law. His trouble was that at night he heard screams which prevented him from sleeping. In fact, he told us that for the last few weeks before going to bed he shut the shutters and stopped up all the windows (it was summer) to the complete despair of his wife, who was stifled by the heat. Moreover, he stuffed his ears with cotton wool in order to make the screams seem less piercing. He sometimes even in the middle of the night turned on the wireless or put on some music in order not to hear this nocturnal uproar. He consequently explained to us at full length the whole story that was troubling him.

A few months before, he had been transferred to an anti-FLN[1] brigade. At the beginning he was entrusted with surveying certain shops or cafés, but after some weeks he used to work almost exclusively at the police headquarters. Here he came to deal with interrogations, and these never occurred without some "knocking about."

"The thing was that they never would own up to anything." He

[1] The FLN was an organization of Algerian patriots who fought for Algerian independence from France.

explained, "Sometimes we almost wanted to tell them that if they had a bit of consideration for us they'd speak out without forcing us to spend hours tearing information word by word out of them. But you might as well talk to the wall. To all the questions we asked they'd only say 'I don't know.' Even when we asked them what their name was. If we asked them where they lived, they'd say 'I don't know.' So of course, we have to go through with it.

"But they scream too much. At the beginning that made me laugh. But afterward I was a bit shaken. Nowadays as soon as I hear someone shouting I can tell you exactly at what stage of the questioning we've got to. The chap who's had two blows of the fist and a belt of the baton behind his ear has a certain way of speaking, of shouting, and of saying he's innocent. After he's been left two hours strung up by his wrists he has another kind of voice. After the bath, still another. And so on. But above all it's after the electricity that it becomes really too much. You'd say that the chap was going to die any minute.

"Of course there are some that don't scream; those are the tough ones. But they think they're going to be killed right away. But we're not interested in killing them. What we want is information. When we're dealing with those tough ones, the first thing we do is to make them squeal; and sooner or later we manage it. That's already a victory. Afterward we go on. Mind you, we'd like to avoid that. But they don't make things easy for us.

"Now I've come so as I hear their screams even when I'm at home. Especially the screams of the ones who died at the police headquarters. Doctor, I'm fed up with this job. And if you manage to cure me, I'll ask to be transferred to France. If they refuse, I'll resign. . . ."

Faced with such a picture, I prescribed sick leave. As the patient in question refused to go to the hospital, I treated him privately. One day, shortly before the therapeutic treatment was due to begin, I had an urgent call from my department. When A—— reached my house, my wife asked him to wait for me, but he preferred to go for a walk in the hospital grounds and then come back to meet me. A few minutes later, as I was going home, I passed him on the way. He was leaning against a tree, looking overcome, trembling and drenched with sweat: in fact, having an anxiety crisis.

I took him into my car and drove him to my house. Once he was lying on the sofa, he told me he had met one of my patients in the hospital who had been questioned in the police barracks (he was an Algerian patriot) and who was under treatment for "disorders of a stuporous nature following on shock." I then learned that the policeman had taken an active part in inflicting torture on my patient.

I administered some sedatives which calmed A——'s anxiety. After he had gone, I went to the house in the hospital where the patriot was being cared for. The personnel had noticed nothing; but the patient could not be found. Finally we managed to discover him in a toilet where he was trying to commit suicide. He on his side had recognized the policeman and thought that he had come to look for him and take him back again to the barracks.

Afterward, A—— came back to see me several times, and after a very definite improvement in his condition, managed to get back to France on account of his health. As for the Algerian patriot, the personnel spent a long time convincing him that the whole thing was an illusion, that policemen were not allowed inside the hospital, that he was very tired, that he was there to be looked after, and so on. . . .

Case Number 2   *The murder by two young Algerians, thirteen and fourteen years old respectively, of their European playmate.*

We had been asked to give expert medical advice in a legal matter. Two young Algerians thirteen and fourteen years old, pupils in a primary school, were accused of having killed one of their European schoolmates. They admitted having done it. The crime was reconstructed, and photos were added to the record. Here one of the children could be seen holding the victim while the other struck at him with a knife. The little defendants did not go back on their declarations. We had long conversations with them. We here reproduce the most characteristic of their remarks:

The boy thirteen years old:
"We weren't a bit cross with him. Every Thursday we used to go and play with catapults together on the hill above the village. He was a good friend of ours. He didn't go to school any more because he wanted to be a mason like his father. One day we decided to kill him, because the Europeans want to kill all the Arabs. We can't kill big people. But we could kill ones like him, because he was the same age as us. We didn't know how to kill him. We wanted to throw him into a ditch, but he'd only have been hurt. So we got the knife from home and we killed him."

"But why did you pick on him?"

"Because he used to play with us. Another boy wouldn't have gone up the hill with us."

"And yet you were pals?"

"Well then, why do they want to kill us? His father is in the militia, and he said we ought to have our throats cut."

"But he didn't say anything to you?"

"Him? No."

"You know he is dead now."

"Yes."

"What does being dead mean?"

"When it's all finished, you go to heaven."

"Was it you that killed him?"

"Yes."

"Does having killed somebody worry you?"

"No, since they want to kill us, so. . . ."

"Do you mind being in prison?"

"No."

The boy fourteen years old:

This young defendant was in marked contrast to his schoolfellow. He was already almost a man, and an adult in his muscular control, his appearance, and the content of his replies. He did not deny having killed either. Why had he killed? He did not reply to the question but asked me had I ever seen a European in prison. Had there ever been a European arrested and sent to prison after the murder of an Algerian? I replied that in fact I had never seen any Europeans in prison.

"And yet there are Algerians killed every day, aren't there?"

"Yes."

"So why are only Algerians found in the prisons? Can you explain that to me?"

"No. But tell me why you killed this boy who was your friend."

"I'll tell you why. You've heard tell of the Rivet business?"[1]

"Yes."

"Two of my family were killed then. At home, they said that the French had sworn to kill us all, one after the other. And did they arrest a single Frenchman for all those Algerians who were killed?"

"I don't know."

"Well, nobody at all was arrested. I wanted to take to the mountains, but I was too young. So X—— and I said we'd kill a European."

"Why?"

"In your opinion, what should we have done?"

"I don't know. But you are a child and what is happening concerns grown-up people."

"But they kill children too. . . ."

"That is no reason for killing your friend."

"Well, kill him I did. Now you can do what you like."

"Had your friend done anything to harm you?"

"Not a thing."

"Well?"

"Well, there you are. . . ."

Translated by Constance Farrington

---

[1] Rivet is a village which has become celebrated in the region around Algiers. In 1956 the village was invaded by the militia, who dragged forty men from their beds and afterward murdered them.

Courtesy Call

DAZAI OSAMU

I

Until the day of my death I shall not forget the man who came to my house that afternoon last September. Although on the surface there may have been nothing very spectacular about his visit, I am convinced that it was a momentous event in my life. For to me this man foretold a new species of humanity. During my years in Tokyo, I had frequented the lowest class of drinking house and mixed with some quite appalling rogues. But this man was in a category all his own: he was far and away the most disagreeable, the most loathsome person I had ever met; there was not a jot of goodness in him.

"I'll be damned," he said, when I opened the door. "If it isn't old Osamu himself!"

I looked at him blankly.

"Come, come," he said, laughing and showing a set of sharp, white teeth, "don't say you've forgotten me! I'm Hirata, your old friend from primary school."

From the dim recesses of my memory there emerged some vague recollection of the face. We may indeed have known each other in school, but as for being old friends, I was not so sure.

"Of course I remember you," I said. "Do come in, Mr. Hirata."

He removed his clogs and strode into the living room.

"Well, well," he said loudly, "it's been a long time, hasn't it?"

"Yes, years and years."

"Years?" he shouted. "Decades, you mean! It must be over twenty years since I saw you. I heard some time ago that you'd moved to our village but I've been far too busy on the farm to call. By the way, they tell me you've become quite a tippler. Spend most of your time at the bottle, eh? Ha, ha, ha!"

I forced a smile and puffed at my cigarette.

"D' you remember how we used to fight at school?" he said, starting on a new tack. "We were always fighting, you and me."

"Were we really?"

"Were we really, indeed!" he said, mimicking my intonation. "Of course we were! I've got a scar here on the back of my hand to remind me. You gave me this scar."

He held out his hand for me to examine, but I could see nothing that even vaguely resembled a scar.

"And what about that one on your left shin? You remember where I hit you with a stone. I bet you've still got a nasty scar to show for it."

I did not have the slightest mark on either of my shins. I smiled vaguely and looked at his large face with its shrewd eyes and fleshy lips.

"Well, so much for all that," he said. "Now I'll tell you why I've come. I want you and me to organize a class reunion. I'll get together about twenty of the lads and we'll have ten gallons of sake. It'll be a real drinking bout. Not such a bad idea, eh?"

"No," I said dubiously. "But isn't ten gallons rather a lot?"

"Of course not," he said. "To have a good time, you want at least eight pints a head."

"Where are you going to buy ten gallons of sake these days?" I said. "One's lucky to find a single bottle."

"Don't worry about that," he said. "I know where I can lay my hands on the stuff. But it's expensive, you know, even here in the country. That's where I want you to help out."

I stood up with a knowing smile. So it was as simple as all that, I thought almost with relief. I went to the back room and returned with a couple of bank notes.

"Here you are," I said.

"Oh no," he said, "I didn't come here today to get money. I came to discuss the class reunion. I wanted to hear your ideas. Besides, I wanted to see my old pal again after all these years. . . . Anyhow that won't be nearly enough. We'll need at least a thousand yen. You can put those notes away."

"Really?" I said, replacing the money in my wallet.

"What about something to drink?" he said all of a sudden.

I looked at him coldly, but he stood his ground.

"Come on," he said, "you needn't look as if you'd never heard of the stuff! They tell me you've always got a good supply put away. Let's have a little drink together! Call the missus! She can pour for us."

"All right," I said, standing up, "come with me." From that moment I was lost.

I led him to the back room, which I used as my study.

"I'm afraid it's in a bit of a mess," I said.

"It doesn't matter," he answered tolerantly. "Scholars' rooms are always like pigsties. I used to know quite a few of you bookworms in my Tokyo days."

I went to the cupboard and took out a bottle of good whisky, which was about half full.

"I don't have any sake," I said. "I hope you won't mind some whisky."

"It'll do," he said. "But I want your little woman to pour the stuff."

"I'm sorry but my wife isn't at home," I said.

In fact she was in the bedroom, but I was determined to spare her this ordeal. Besides, I felt sure that the farmer would be disappointed in her. He would no doubt expect a smart, sophisticated woman from the city and, although my wife was born and bred in Tokyo, she had about her something rustic, almost gauche.

But the deception did not escape my visitor.

"Of course she's at home," he said. "Tell her to come and do the pouring."

I decided simply to ignore his request and, filling a teacup with whisky, handed it to him.

"I'm afraid it's not quite up to prewar quality," I said.

He tossed it off at a single draught, smacked his lips loudly and said: "It's pretty cheap stuff, isn't it?"

"I'm sorry, but it's the best I can get. . . . I wouldn't drink it down too quickly if I were you," I added.

"The bottle's almost empty," he announced.

"Oh, really?" I said, assuming a nonchalance that I was far from feeling. I took another bottle out of the cupboard.

The man continued drinking and, as the level of the whisky in the second bottle began to sink, I finally felt anger rise within me. It was not that I was usually jealous about my property. Far from it. Having lost almost all my possessions in the bombings, what was left meant hardly anything to me. But this whisky was an exception. I had obtained it some time before at immense difficulty and expense, and had rationed myself severely, only now and then sipping a small glass after dinner.

I suddenly wanted to ask him to leave. Yet the fact was that I did not dare to. Our position in this village was far from secure and I could not risk offending someone who appeared to be an old and well-established inhabitant. Besides, I was afraid that if I asked him to go, he might think that I looked down on him for being an uneducated farmer.

He examined his empty cup pensively and then all of a sudden shouted, "Call in the little woman! I won't drink another drop unless she pours it for me herself. Not another drop, d' you hear?" He staggered to his feet. "Where is the little woman, anyway? In the bedroom, I expect; snug in bed, eh? D'you know who I am? I'm Hirata, I'm a lord among farmers! Haven't you heard of the great Hirata family?"

My worst fears were being realized and I saw that there was nothing for it but to fetch my wife.

"Do sit down, Mr. Hirata," I said calmly. "I'll call her right away, if it means all that much to you."

II

I went into the bedroom, where my wife was busy darning some socks.

"Would you mind coming in for a minute?" I asked her casually. "An old schoolfriend has come to see me." I said no more, as I did not want my wife to be prejudiced in advance against the visitor. In particular I did not want her to think that I considered him in any way inferior to us. She nodded and followed me into the back room.

"Let me introduce Mr. Hirata," I said, "my old friend from primary school. We were always fighting when we were kids. He's got a mark on the back of his hand where I scratched him. Today he's come to get his revenge."

"How terrifying!" she said, laughing. "Anyhow, I'm glad to meet you." She bowed in his direction.

Our visitor seemed to relish these courtesies.

"Glad to meet you, Madam," he said. "But you needn't stand on ceremony with me. By the way, I'd very much appreciate it if you'd pour me some whisky."

I noticed that he was sober enough to address my wife politely, although a few moments before he had been referring to her as "the little woman."

"You know, Madam," he said, when my wife had filled his cup, "I was just telling Osamu here that if you ever need any food, be sure to come round to my place. I've got plenty of everything: potatoes, vegetables, rice, eggs, chickens. Do you like pheasant? Of course you do! Well, I'm the most famous shot in these parts. Just tell me what you want and I'll shoot it. Maybe Madam would fancy some nice wild duck. Right, I'll go out tomorrow morning and shoot a dozen for you. That's nothing—a dozen. I've shot five dozen before breakfast in my day. If you don't believe me, ask anyone round here. I'm the greatest marksman in the district."

"Please go and fetch some cakes," I said to my wife, with a sigh.

"I imagine you're going back to Tokyo pretty soon," said Mr. Hirata, as my wife left the room. "Where do you live in Tokyo?"

"I lost my house in the war."

"So you were bombed out, were you? That's the first I've heard of it. Well, in that case you must have got that special allocation of a blanket that they gave each family of evacuees. Would you mind letting me have it?"

I looked at him with renewed amazement.

"That's right," he said, calmly refilling his cup. "Give me the blanket. It's meant to be quite good wool. My wife can make me a jumper with it. . . . I suppose you think it's funny of me to ask you for the blanket like this. But that's the way I do things. If I want something, I just ask for it. And when you come to my place, you can do the same. I'll give you whatever you like. What's the use of standing on ceremony with each other? Well, what about it? Are you going to let me have that blanket?"

I still stared at him blankly. This wool blanket, which we had been given as a sort of consolation prize, seemed to be my wife's most treasured possession. When our house was bombed and we moved to the country with our children, like a family of crabs whose shells have been smashed and who crawl naked and helpless across a hostile beach, she had kept the blanket constantly in sight, as though it were some sort of talisman.

144

The man who now faced me could never know how a family felt who had lost their house in the war, or how close to committing mass suicide such families often were.

"I'm afraid you'll have to forget about the blanket," I said firmly.

"You stingy devil!" he said. "Why can't I have it?"

At this moment I was delighted to see my wife reappear with a tray of cakes. As I expected, our visitor instantly forgot about the blanket.

"Good gracious, Madam," he said, "you shouldn't have gone to all that trouble. I don't want anything to eat. I came here to drink. But I want you to do the pouring from now on. This husband of yours is too stingy for my liking." He glared at me. "What about it, Madam? Shall I give him a good beating? I used to be quite a fighter in my Tokyo days. I know a bit of jujitsu too. He'll be an easy match, even though he may be a few years younger than me. Well, Madam, if he ever gives you any trouble, just tell me and I'll let him have a thrashing he won't forget in a hurry. You see, I've known him since we were boys together at school and he doesn't dare put on any of his airs with me."

III

It was then that the various stories which I had read years ago in textbooks on moral training came back to me—stories about great men who, on being abused by unmannerly rogues like this, did not answer in kind, but instead displayed their true moral superiority, as well as their fathomless contempt for these ruffians, by forthrightly asking them for forgiveness, when by all rights it was they who deserved apology. Until now, rather than admire the much-vaunted patience of these men, I had always tended to despise it as concealing an arrogant sense of superiority; my sympathy had, in fact, been on the side of the so-called rogues, whose behavior was at least natural and unpretentious. But now unexpectedly I found myself in the role of the great men. All of a sudden I knew the sense of isolation which they too must have felt when being attacked. At the same time I perceived that forbearance really had very little to do with the matter. It was simply that these "great men" were weaker than their assailants and knew that they would not stand a chance if it came to a fight. I had a horrible vision of our visitor suddenly running amuck and smashing the screens, sliding doors, and furniture. Since none of the property belonged to me, I lived in a constant state of apprehension that the children might scribble on the walls or push the doors too roughly; the idea of the terrible ravages that this farmer might now perpetrate made cold shivers run down my spine. At all cost, I thought in my lonely cowardice, I must avoid offending him.

Suddenly I heard him roaring at the top of his lungs, "Ho, ho!" I looked up aghast. "I'm drunk!" he shouted. "Yes, damn it, I'm drunk!"

Then he gave a groan, closed his eyes tightly, and planting both elbows on his knees, sat there with a look of complete concentration, as if desperately fighting his drunkenness. The perspiration glistened on his forehead and his face was almost purple. My wife and I looked at each other uneasily. Then, to our amazement, he opened his eyes and said calmly, as if nothing whatever had happened, "When all's said and done, I like an occasional nip of whisky. It makes me feel good. Come over here, Madam, and pour me another cup. Don't worry, us farmers can drink as much as we like without getting tipsy."

Seeing that my wife made no move, he reached for the bottle himself, filled his cup, and drained it at a single draught.

"Well, you've both been very civil," he said, smacking his lips. "Next time you must be my guests. The trouble is, though, I really don't know what I'd give you if you did come to my place. . . ." His words trailed off into a murmur and for a while he was silent.

"I've really got nothing in my place," he continued, "nothing at all. That's why I came here today for a drink. Of course, I could try to shoot a wild duck. We'd eat it together—just the three of us—and Osamu here would provide the whisky. But I'll do it only on one condition: while you're eating it you've got to keep saying, 'How delicious! What a splendid duck!' If you don't, I'll be furious. In fact I'll never forgive you. Ha, ha, ha! Yes, Madam, that's the way we farmers are. Treat us right and there's nothing in the world we won't do for you. But if you're snooty and standoffish, we won't give you as much as a piece of string. No use putting on airs with me, Madam."

My wife laughed good-naturedly and stood up. "I'm afraid I'll have to leave you," she said. "I hear the baby crying."

"She's no good!" he shouted, as soon as my wife had left the room. "Your missus is no good, I tell you! Now take my old woman, for instance. There's a real wife for you! We've got six lovely kids and we're as happy a family as you'll find anywhere in these parts. Ask anyone in the village if you don't believe me." He glared at me defiantly. "Well, I'm off," he said, getting slowly to his feet. "Your missus has left and I don't enjoy drinking the whisky when you pour it."

I did not try to detain him.

"We'll discuss the class reunion when I have more time," he said. "I'll have to leave most of the arrangements to you. In the meantime you can let me have a little of your whisky to take home."

I was prepared for this and immediately started to pour the whisky that remained in his cup into the bottle, which was still about a quarter full.

"You can have this bottle," I said, handing it to him.

"Hey, hey," he said, "none of that! I've had enough of your stinginess for one day. You've still got another full bottle stored away in that cupboard, haven't you? Let me have it!"

"All right," I said.

There was nothing for it but to hand over my final bottle of whisky. At least this put the proper finishing touch to the afternoon, I thought with a bitter smile. Now if Mr. Ibusé or any other friend came to visit, we would no longer be able to enjoy a convivial drink. For a moment I thought of mentioning the cost of whisky, just to see what reaction it would bring, but even now I could not bring myself to violate the code of a host. Instead I heard myself asking ignominiously, "What about cigarettes? Do you need any cigarettes?"

"I'll get those next time," he said, picking up a whisky bottle in each hand.

I followed him to the front door and here it was that the climax of the visit came. As he was about to step out of the door, he hiccuped loudly, turned round, and hissed into my ear, "You shouldn't be so damned stuck-up!"

Yes, he was a man of truly epic proportions.

Translated by Ivan Morris

THE WAGES

In the middle of the day, a child who was gathering dead wood found Diassigue-the-Alligator in the scrub.

"What are you doing there, Diassigue?" asked the child.

"I have lost my way," answered the alligator. "Will you carry me home, Goné?"

Goné-the-Child went to fetch a mat and some creepers. He rolled Diassigue up in the mat, which he fastened with the creepers. Then he put it on his head and walked until the evening, when he reached the river. Arriving at the water's edge, he put down his bundle, cut the creepers, and unrolled the mat.

Then Diassigue said to him, "Goné, my legs are all stiff from that long journey. Will you put me into the water, please?"

Goné-the-Child walked into the water until it came up to his knees, and he was about to put Diassigue down when the alligator said to him, "Go on until the water comes up to your waist, for I would find it hard to swim here."

Goné did as he asked and walked on until the water encircled his waist.

"Go on until it comes up to your chest," the alligator begged him.

The child went on until the water reached his chest.

"You might as well go on now until it comes up to your shoulders."

Goné walked on until his shoulders were covered, and then Diassigue said to him, "Now put me down."

Goné obeyed. He was about to return to the river bank when the alligator gripped him by the arm.

OF GOOD

BIRAGO DIOP

"*Wouye yayô!* Oh, Mother," cried the child. "What are you doing? Let go of me!"

"I shan't let go of you, because I'm very hungry, Goné."

"Let go of me!"

"I shan't let go of you. I haven't had anything to eat for two days and I'm too hungry."

"Tell me, Diassigue, do you repay a kindness with another kindness or with a bad turn?"

"A good deed is repaid with a bad turn and not with another good deed."

"Now it's I who am in your power, but what you say isn't true, and you must be the only person in the whole world to say it."

"Oh! You really think so?"

"Well, let's ask a few people and we'll see what they say."

"All right," said Diassigue, "but if we find three people who share my opinion, then you'll end up in my stomach, I promise you."

He had scarcely finished uttering this threat when an old, old cow arrived to drink out of the river. When she had quenched her thirst, the alligator called her and asked her, "Nagy, you who are so old and possess all wisdom, can you tell us whether a good deed is repaid with a kindness or with a bad turn?"

"A good deed," declared Nagy-the-Cow, "is repaid with a bad turn, and believe me, I know what I'm talking about. In the days when I was young, strong, and vigorous, when I came back from the pasture I was given bran, millet and a lump of salt. I was washed and rubbed down, and if Poulo, the little shepherd, happened to raise his stick against me, he was sure to receive a beating in his turn from his master. At that time I gave a lot of milk, and all my master's cows and bulls are offspring of mine. Now I am old and no longer give any milk or calves, so nobody takes care of me any more or takes me out to graze. At dawn every day, a blow from a stick drives me out of the park, and I go off on my own to look for my food. That is why I say that a good deed is repaid with a bad turn."

"Goné, did you hear that?" asked Diassigue-the-Alligator.

"Yes," said the child, "I heard it all right."

Then gaunt old Fass-the-Horse arrived on the scene. He was about to brush the water with his lips before drinking when the alligator called out to him, "Fass, you who are so old and wise, can you tell us, this child and me, whether a good deed is repaid with a kindness or with a bad turn?"

"I certainly can," declared the old horse. "A kindness is always repaid by an evil deed, and I know something about it. Listen to me, the two of you. In the days when I was young, strong and high-spirited, I had three grooms all to myself. I had my trough filled with millet morning and night, and bran mash often mixed with honey at all hours of the day. I was taken for a bath and a rub-down every morning. I had a bridle and a saddle made by a Moorish saddler and adorned by a Moorish jeweler. I used to go on the battlefields, and the five hundred prisoners my master took in the wars were brought back on my harness. For nine years I carried my master and his booty. Now that I have grown old, all that they do for me is hobble me at dawn, and then, with a blow from a stick, they send me into the scrubland to look for my food."

"Goné," said the alligator, "did you hear that? Now I'm too hungry to wait any longer; I'm going to eat you."

"No, Uncle Diassigue," said the child. "You said yourself that you would ask three people. If the next person who comes along says the same as those two, then you can eat me, but not before."

"Very well," agreed the alligator, "but I warn you that we shan't go any further afield."

Then Leuk-the-Hare came running up, his hindquarters twitching. Diassigue called him. "Uncle Leuk, you who are the oldest among us, can you tell us which of us two is right? I say that a good deed is repaid with a bad turn, and this child declares that the price of a good deed is a kindness."

Leuk rubbed his chin, scratched his ear, and then asked in his turn, "Diassigue, my friend, do you ask a blind man to tell you whether cotton is white or whether a crow is really black?"

"Of course not," admitted the alligator.

"Then explain to me what has happened and I may be able to answer your question without much risk of making a mistake."

"Well, Uncle Leuk, this is the position: This child found me, rolled me up in a mat and carried me here. Now I'm feeling hungry, and seeing that I have to eat because I don't want to die, it would be stupid of me to let him go."

"Indubitably," said Leuk, "but when words are sick, ears have to be healthy, and my ears, to the best of my knowledge, are perfectly well, thank God, for there are some of your words, Brother Diassigue, which don't strike me as being in very good health."

"Which words are those?" asked the alligator.

"It's when you say that this little boy carried you in a mat and brought you all the way here. I can't believe that."

"All the same, it's true," declared Goné-the-Child.

"You're a liar like the rest of your race," said the hare.

"He is telling the truth," confirmed Diassigue.

"I can't believe that unless I see it," said Leuk incredulously. "Get out of the water, both of you."

The child and the alligator came out of the water.

"You claim to have carried this big alligator in that mat? How did you do it?"

"I rolled him up in it and then tied it up."

"Well, I want to see how."

Diassigue lay down on the mat, and the child rolled it up.

"And you say that you tied it up?"

"Yes."

"Tie it up to show me."

The child tied the mat up securely.

"And you carried him on your head?"

"Yes, I carried him on my head."

"Well, carry him on your head so that I can see."

When the child had lifted up mat and alligator and placed them on his head, Leuk-the-Hare asked him, "Goné, are your family blacksmiths?"

"No."

"So Diassigue isn't a relative of yours? He isn't your totem?"

"No, certainly not."

"Then take your bundle home. Your father and your mother and all your relatives and their friends will thank you, since you can eat alligator at home. That is how to repay those who forget a good deed."

Translated by Robert Baldick

THOSE THAT HAVE NOT EXPLODED

THICH NHAT HANH

I don't know why,
I don't know what made my countrymen
hurl grenades
at my brothers and sisters.

Why wish to kill
those boys with still pure brows
those girls from school with ink-stained hands?

What crime was theirs?
To hear the voice of compassion?
To do this:
Live in the hamlet
Help the villagers
Teach the children
Work in the paddies.

Last night
when those grenades burst
twelve students fell
with mangled bodies and burst skin.
One girl's flesh took sixty metal bits.

This morning, two are buried
and each one waits for dawn again
within his motherland.
Each waits for peace within his motherland
and reincarnation as a butterfly.

And so we have accepted death and sorrow.
But hear me, O sisters and brothers,
those grenades have burst and ripped apart the sky now,
those boys and girls have gone,
trailing their blood.

152

But there are more grenades
than those which burst last night.
But there are more grenades
and these are caught in the heart of life.
Do you hear me?
There are more, and they have not burst.

They remain
still
in the heart of Man.
Unknown, the time of their detonation.
Unknown, when they will desecrate our land.
Unknown, the time they will annihilate our people.
And still,
we beg you to believe
there is no hatred in our hearts
and in our souls no rancor,
because
what the world needs,
what our country needs
is love.

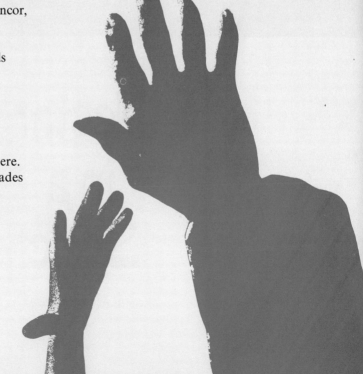

Come.
Hear me.
For time grows short
and danger is everywhere.
Let us take those grenades
out of our hearts,
our motherland,
Mankind.
Let us stand
Let us stand
Side by side.

from Nectar
in a
Sieve

KAMALA MARKANDAYA

Kenny's return was the beginning of another change in our lives, and in Selvam's. Selvam, who for all that he had been reared on the land and had the earth in his blood, yet did not take to farming. Like his brothers, he was hard-working and conscientious, but he had no love for it and in return it did not yield to him. He had a knowledge of crops and seasons, born of experience; but where crops thrived under Nathan's hand, under his they wilted. Despite anxious care, the seed he planted did not sprout, the plants that sprouted did not bear.

One day he came straight from working in the fields, threw down the spade he was carrying and announced he was finished with the land.

"I am no farmer," he said. "The land has no liking for me, and I have no time for it."

"What then will you do, my son?" I said, worried. "How will you live when we are gone?"

He did not reply at once, but sat down cross-legged, looking out absently beyond the small courtyard to the cool green of the paddy fields. But he was not thinking of them.

"Kenny is building a hospital," he said. "When it is ready he will need an assistant, and he has offered me the job."

"But what can you know of such work?"

"Nothing. He is going to train me, starting as soon as possible. He says it will not be too difficult for me, for I am not without learning."

It was true. Selvam had been cast in the same mold as his brothers. He had quickly learned what I had to teach and had progressed from there by his own efforts and enthusiasm. Study came to him naturally; he wrote and read as I had once done, avidly, with pleasure. He will learn, I thought. This is the chance he has been waiting for.

Selvam began to fidget.

"I have told my father," he said hesitantly. "He is very willing."

I smiled at him. "So am I. I wish you well."

He relaxed. "I am glad. I thought you might be—were—displeased."

"Not displeased. Perhaps disappointed, since all our sons have forsaken the land. But it is the best way for you."

"It is the best way," he repeated after me. "It will be a great venture. We have many plans and much hope."

We both relapsed into silence. I watched him covertly, wondering whether I should say, "You must be prepared: this new association will not be taken at face value, there will be vilifiers who will say it was done not for you, but for your mother, who will seek to destroy your peace"; but then I thought resolutely, I will not take the fire from his resolve or sow suspicion between them, and so I held my peace. But his steady eyes were on me, calm and level.

"I am not unaware," he said quietly. "But is it not sufficient that you have the strength and I have trust?"

"It is indeed," I said with relief. "I wanted only that you should know."

We smiled at each other in perfect understanding.

I sought out Kenny again.

"We are once more in your debt. My son is overjoyed. This is something he has waited for without knowing it."

"I am indebted to him as well. I need an assistant; he promises to be a good one and will I hope be the first of many. I could not carry on alone. The town has grown and is still growing, as you know."

"It will be bigger than what went before?"

"It will be a hospital, not a dispensary," he said coldly. "Let me show you."

He pulled out several papers, drawings, and long sheets covered with calculations, which I could not understand even when he explained them, though this I did not confess. I gathered only that it would be a big affair.

"Where is the money to come from?" I said, bewildered. "Such a construction will need I do not know how many hundreds of rupees."

"I have thousands," he replied.

"I did not realize. You have lived like us, the poor."

"The money is not mine. It has been given to me—I have collected it while I have been away."

"In your country?" I said. "From your people?"

"Yes," he said impatiently. "Part of it came from my country and my people, part of it from yours. Why do you look puzzled?"

"I have little understanding," I replied humbly. "I do not know why people who have not seen us and who know us not should do this for us."

"Because they have the means," he said, "and because they have learned of your need. Do not the sick die in the streets because there is no hospital for them? Are not children born in the gutters? I have told you before," he said. "I will repeat it again: you must cry out if you want help. It is no use whatsoever to suffer in silence. Who will succor the drowning man if he does not clamor for his life?"

"It is said—" I began.

"Never mind what is said or what you have been told. There is no grandeur in want—or in endurance."

Privately I thought, Well, and what if we gave in to our troubles at every step! We would be pitiable creatures indeed to be so weak, for is not a man's spirit given to him to rise above his misfortunes? As for our wants, they are many and unfilled, for who is so rich or compassionate as to supply them? Want is our companion from birth to death, familiar as the seasons or the earth, varying only in degree. What profit to bewail that which has always been and cannot change?

His eyes narrowed: whether from our long association, or from many dealings with human beings, and whether one kept silent or spoke to cloak one's thoughts, he always knew the heart of the matter.

"Acquiescent imbeciles," he said scornfully, "do you think spiritual grace comes from being in want, or from suffering? What thoughts have you when your belly is empty or your body is sick? Tell me they are noble ones and I will call you a liar."

"Yet our priests fast, and inflict on themselves severe punishments, and we are taught to bear our sorrows in silence, and all this is so that the soul may be cleansed."

He struck his forehead. "My God!" he cried. "I do not understand you. I never will. Go, before I too am entangled in your philosophies."

A Letter to God

GREGORIO LÓPEZ Y FUENTES

The house—the only one in the entire village—sat on the crest of a low hill. From this height one could see the river and, next to the corral, the field of ripe corn dotted with the kidney bean flowers that always promised a good harvest.

The only thing the earth needed was a rainfall, or at least a shower. Throughout the morning Lencho—who knew his fields intimately—had done nothing else but scan the sky toward the northeast.

"Now we're really going to get some water, woman."

The woman, who was preparing supper, replied:

"Yes, God willing."

The oldest boys were working in the field, while the smaller ones were playing near the house, until the woman called to them all:

"Come for dinner. . . ."

It was during the meal that, just as Lencho had predicted, big drops of rain began to fall. In the northeast huge mountains of clouds could be seen approaching. The air was fresh and sweet.

The man went out to look for something in the corral for no other reason than to allow himself the pleasure of feeling the rain on his body, and when he returned he exclaimed:

"Those aren't raindrops falling from the sky, they're new coins. The big drops are ten-*centavo* pieces and the little ones are fives . . ."

With a satisfied expression he regarded the field of ripe corn with its kidney bean flowers, draped in a curtain of rain. But suddenly a strong wind began to blow and together with the rain very large hailstones began to fall. These truly did resemble new silver coins. The boys, exposing themselves to the rain, ran out to collect the frozen pearls.

"It's really getting bad now," exclaimed the man, mortified. "I hope it passes quickly."

It did not pass quickly. For an hour the hail rained on the house, the garden, the hillside, the cornfield, on the whole valley. The field was white, as if covered with salt. Not a leaf remained on the trees. The corn was totally destroyed. The flowers were gone from the kidney bean plants. Lencho's soul was filled with sadness. When the storm had passed, he stood in the middle of the field and said to his sons:

"A plague of locusts would have left more than this. . . . The hail has left nothing: this year we will have no corn or beans. . . ."

That night was a sorrowful one:

"All our work, for nothing!"

"There's no one who can help us!"

"We'll all go hungry this year. . . ."

But in the hearts of all who lived in that solitary house in the middle of the valley, there was a single hope: help from God.

"Don't be so upset, even though this seems like a total loss. Remember, no one dies of hunger!"

"That's what they say: no one dies of hunger. . . ."

All through the night, Lencho thought only of his one hope: the help of God, whose eyes, as he had been instructed, see everything, even what is deep in one's conscience.

Lencho was an ox of a man, working like an animal in the fields, but still he knew how to write. The following Sunday, at daybreak, after having convinced himself that there is a protecting spirit, he began to write a letter which he himself would carry to town and place in the mail.

It was nothing less than a letter to God.

"God," he wrote, "if you don't help me, my family and I will go hungry this year. I need a hundred *pesos* in order to resow the field and to live until the crop comes, because the hailstorm . . ."

He wrote "To God" on the envelope, put the letter inside and, still troubled, went to town. At the post office he placed a stamp on the letter and dropped it into the mailbox.

One of the employees, who was a postman and also helped at the post office, went to his boss laughing heartily and showed him the letter to God. Never in his career as a postman had he known that address. The postmaster—a fat, amiable fellow—also broke out laughing, but almost immediately he turned serious and, tapping the letter on his desk, commented:

"What faith! I wish I had the faith of the man who wrote this letter. To believe the way he believes. To hope with the confidence that he knows how to hope with. Starting up a correspondence with God!"

So, in order not to disillusion that prodigy of faith, revealed by a letter that could not be delivered, the postmaster came up with an idea: answer the letter. But when he opened it, it was evident that to answer it he needed something more than good will, ink and paper. But he stuck to his resolution: he asked for money from his employees, he himself gave part of his salary, and several friends of his were obliged to give something "for an act of charity."

It was impossible for him to gather together the hundred *pesos* requested by Lencho, so he was able to send the farmer only a little more than half. He put the bills in an envelope addressed to Lencho and with them a letter containing only a single word as a signature: God.

The following Sunday Lencho came a bit earlier than usual to ask if there was a letter for him. It was the postman himself who handed the letter to him, while the postmaster, experiencing the contentment of a man who has performed a good deed, looked on from the doorway of his office.

Lencho showed not the slightest surprise on seeing the bills—such was his confidence—but he became angry when he counted the money ... God could not have made a mistake, nor could he have denied Lencho what he had requested!

Immediately, Lencho went up to the window to ask for paper and ink. On the public writing table, he started in to write, with much wrinkling of his brow, caused by the effort he had to make to express his ideas. When he finished, he went to the window to buy a stamp which he licked and then affixed to the envelope with a blow of his fist.

The moment that the letter fell into the mailbox the postmaster went to open it. It said:

"God: of the money that I asked for, only seventy *pesos* reached me. Send me the rest, since I need it very much. But don't send it to me through the mail, because the post office employees are a bunch of crooks. Lencho."

Translated by Donald A. Yates

160

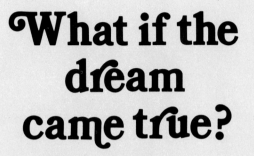

What if the dream came true?

I have squandered the splendid years
that the Lord gave to my youth
In attempting impossible things
deeming them alone worth the toil.

The lawyers have sat in council,
the men with the keen long faces,
and said, "This man is a fool,"
and others have said, "He blasphemeth."

O wise men riddle me this:
What if the dream came true?

Metrical chant by Padraic Pearse (Ireland).

from

A Taste of Honey

SHELAGH DELANEY

(JO *and her* BOY FRIEND, *walking on the street. They stop by the door.*)

JO. I'd better go in now. Thanks for carrying my books.

BOY. Were you surprised to see me waiting outside school?

JO. Not really.

BOY. Glad I came?

JO. You know I am.

BOY. So am I.

JO. Well, I'd better go in.

BOY. Not yet! Stay a bit longer.

JO. All right! Doesn't it go dark early? I like winter. I like it better than all the other seasons.

BOY. I like it too. When it goes dark early it gives me more time for— (*He kisses her.*)

JO. Don't do that. You're always doing it.

BOY. You like it.

JO. I know, but I don't want to do it all the time.

BOY. Afraid someone'll see us?

JO. I don't care.

BOY. Say that again.

JO. I don't care.

BOY. You mean it too. You're the first girl I've met who really didn't care. Listen, I'm going to ask you something. I'm a man of few words. Will you marry me?

JO. Well, I'm a girl of few words. I won't marry you but you've talked me into it.

BOY. How old are you?

JO. Nearly eighteen.

BOY. And you really will marry me?

JO. I said so, didn't I? You shouldn't have asked me if you were only kidding me up. (*She starts to go.*)

BOY. Hey! I wasn't kidding. I thought you were. Do you really mean it? You will marry me?

JO. I love you.

BOY. How do you know?

JO. I don't know why I love you but I do.

BOY. I adore you. (*Swinging her through the air.*)

JO. So do I. I can't resist myself.

BOY. I've got something for you.

JO. What is it? A ring!

BOY. This morning in the shop I couldn't remember what sort of hands you had, long hands, small hands or what. I stood there like a fool trying to remember what they felt like. (*He puts the ring on and kisses her hand.*) What will your mother say?

JO. She'll probably laugh.

BOY. Doesn't she care who her daughter marries?

JO. She's not marrying you; I am. It's got nothing to do with her.

BOY. She hasn't seen me.

JO. And when she does?

BOY. She'll see a colored boy.

JO. No, whatever else she might be, she isn't prejudiced against color. You're not worried about it, are you?

BOY. So long as you like it.

JO. You know I do.

BOY. Well, that's all that matters.

JO. When shall we get married?

BOY. My next leave? It's a long time, six months.

JO. It'll give us a chance to save a bit of money. Here, see . . . this ring
. . . it's too big; look, it slides about. . . . And I couldn't wear it for
school anyway. I might lose it. Let's go all romantic. Have you got
a bit of string?

BOY. What for?

JO. I'm going to tie it round my neck. Come on, turn your pockets out.
Three handkerchiefs, a safety pin, a screw! Did that drop out of your
head? Elastic bands! Don't little boys carry some trash. And what's
this?

BOY. Nothing.

JO. A toy car! Does it go?

BOY. Hm hm!

JO. Can I try it? (*She does.*)

BOY. She doesn't even know how it works. Look, not like that. (*He makes
it go fast.*)

JO. I like that. Can I keep it?

BOY. Yes, take it, my soul and all, everything.

JO. Thanks. I know, I can use my hair ribbon for my ring. Do it up for
me.

BOY. Pretty neck you've got.

JO. Glad you like it. It's my schoolgirl complexion. I'd better tuck this
out of sight. I don't want my mother to see it. She'd only laugh. Did
I tell you, when I leave school this week I start a part-time job in
a bar? Then as soon as I get a full-time job, I'm leaving Helen and
starting up in a room somewhere.

BOY. I wish I wasn't in the Navy.

JO. Why?

BOY. We won't have much time together.

JO. Well, we can't be together all the time and all the time there is wouldn't
be enough.

BOY. It's a sad story, Jo. Once, I was a happy young man, not a care
in the world. Now! I'm trapped into a barbaric cult. . . .

JO. What's that? Mau-Mau?

BOY. Matrimony.

JO. Trapped! I like that! You almost begged me to marry you. . . .

BOY. You led me on. I'm a trusting soul. Who took me down to that
deserted football pitch?

JO. Who found the football pitch? I didn't even know it existed. And it
just shows how often you must have been there, too . . . you certainly
know where all the best spots are. I'm not going there again . . . It's
too quiet. Anything might happen to a girl.

BOY. It almost did. You shameless woman!

JO. That's you taking advantage of my innocence.

BOY. I didn't take advantage. I had scruples.

JO. You would have done. You'd have gone as far as I would have let you and no scruples would have stood in your way.

BOY. You enjoyed it as much as I did.

JO. Shut up! This is the sort of conversation that can color a young girl's mind.

BOY. Women never have young minds. They are born three thousand years old.

JO. Sometimes you look three thousand years old. Did your ancestors come from Africa?

BOY. No. Cardiff. Disappointed? Were you hoping to marry a man whose father beat the tom-tom all night?

JO. I don't care where you were born. There's still a bit of jungle in you somewhere. (*A siren is heard.*) I'm going in now, I'm hungry. A young girl's got to eat, you know.

BOY. Honey, you've got to stop eating. No more food, no more make-up, no more fancy clothes; we're saving up to get married.

JO. I just need some new clothes too. I've only got this one coat. I have to use it for school and when I go out with you. I do feel a mess.

BOY. You look all right to me.

JO. Shall I see you tonight?

BOY. No, I got work to do.

JO. What sort of work?

BOY. Hard work, it involves a lot of walking.

JO. And a lot of walking makes you thirsty. I know; you're going drinking.

BOY. That's right. It's one of the lads' birthdays. I'll see you tomorrow.

JO. All right. I'll tell you what, I won't bother going to school and we can spend the whole day together. I'll meet you down by that ladies' hairdressing place.

BOY. The place that smells of cooking hair?

JO. Yes, about ten o'clock.

BOY. OK, you're the boss.

JO. Good night.

BOY. Aren't you going to kiss me good night?

JO. You know I am. (*Kisses him*) I like kissing you. Good night.

BOY. Good night.

JO. Dream of me.

BOY. I dreamt about you last night. Fell out of bed twice.

JO. You're in a bad way.

BOY. You bet I am. Be seeing you!

JO (*as she goes*). I love you.

BOY. Why?

JO. Because you're daft. (*He waves good-by.* JO *dances on dreamily.*)

Nobody Home

ROQUE VALLEJOS

There are times when no one
remembers
that we exist;
when life shrinks
and is too small for us,
when it is hard to arouse
the blood in our veins every morning,

       Days of talking
with our skeleton, folding inward,
and weeping in the dark
over these sad bones,
of wearing our own skin
for a shroud, and telling
life there's nobody home:
come back some other day.

               Translated by John Upton

Inn of
Synthetic
Dreams

ANDREAS JACOB

The hotel is in Kabul, Afghanistan. It is one of the most remarkable in a chain of very unusual lodging places stretching from Istanbul to Katmandu. It was built about sixty years ago, and the architecture is vaguely classical. At that time, there were probably no more than ten solidly built homes in all of Kabul.

You walk through a gate and find yourself in the hotel garden—here are cantaloupe beds, two large sofas, some chairs, and a table within a bower. Only someone who is familiar with the pungent, earthy aroma that fills the air could explain the dazed but blissful expression on the young people's faces.

In one corner a young Englishman is banging away on the bongo drums—he has been at it all night long—while a compatriot accompanies him on the flute. The gardeners, clad in turbans and pajama bottoms, are running around with hoses, watering the cantaloupes. An American girl, draped in a flimsy sari, is trying to wash her companion's trousers in the fountain. Completely enclosed by a mosquito net, an American boy lies fast asleep on a Persian rug in the middle of a cantaloupe patch. From the direction of the hotel's main entrance comes the roar and blare of Kabul traffic. The owner of the hotel lives in a small wooden cabin right in the middle of the garden, so that he can keep a close watch on the exit; quite a few people have left without paying their bills.

It is 11 o'clock in the morning. A few of the guests are beginning to stir. They all belong to that species which people, without regard to fine distinctions, call hippies or beatniks, although it is hard to classify them on the basis of their external appearance alone. They all have certain things in common, it seems: very little baggage, very little money, very long hair, and a dreamy nonchalance that appears to be boundless. Most of them are students who, every year, come to Kabul by plane and spend a very restful summer vacation in this hotel "smoking" to their heart's content. Some of them have been here four times already.

What distinguishes this hotel from all others, what makes it so special in the eyes of its guests, is the fact that smoking hashish and "shooting" opium are more or less legal in Afghanistan, whereas, in every other country, these things are forbidden by stringent laws.

I spent some time with a few Parisian students in one of the huts in the garden. For 20 afghanis (25 cents), you can stay there overnight, if you are willing to sleep on the floor. A bit inconvenient perhaps, but after smoking your evening water pipe, you are so tired (though in a pleasant sort of way) that you hardly notice the ground is hard.

There is a mobile suspended from the ceiling, slowly turning. Each of its parts represents a facet of the dreamlike existence of these people, who have left normal society for a world of drugs and a communal life free of pressure. A small box of "Maxiton Fort" capsules, one of the strongest of the amphetamines, dangles on a string next to an empty package of a cough medicine which, if taken in the "correct" dosage (here, that means in large quantity), produces a "trip" during which incredible intense colors and patterns flash before one's eyes; while the other "ornaments"—little boxes of morphine, empty capsules, and a lump of solid black opium—perform a grotesque and aimless dance in midair.

The amphetamines, drugs peculiar to our mechanized world, are very highly rated. "You will never forget your first Maxiton trip," the students say. The six-hour opening phase and the six-hour "descent" are equally exhausting and nerve-shattering for the "head"; and, afterward, completely drained, he will collapse into a profound sleep.

It is easy to spot those guests in the garden who are under the influence of narcotics. They are the ones who move like robots, who with mechanical regularity are perpetually brushing an imaginary lock of hair out of their eyes; or the ones who, like an inexorable machine, strum their guitars all night long—twelve hours straight without a pause.

People are babbling in French, English, or German. Someone starts playing the bongo drums. The others stumble through the door and either stagger around the cantaloupe patch or become entangled in the mesh of the mosquito net. But things stay calm—everyone is too lethargically happy to start a quarrel.

Hashish is one of the things that makes people want to come to Afghanistan, not only because smoking the stuff was perfectly legal up till a year ago, but also because, in the opinion of connoisseurs, Afghan hashish compares quite favorably, from the point of view of quality, with the Nepalese variety. This situation is too tempting for smugglers to resist. Whereas, in Kabul, a kilo may cost no more than a few dollars (even less in Kandahar), the same quantity will bring $1,200 in Copenhagen. In Kabul and Kandahar, there are "craft guilds" specializing in the packaging of hashish.

For example, in Kandahar, if you buy a can of American pineapple, you may find some hashish inside (but the can will still have the correct weight). Some physicians, they say, used to insert hashish into the plaster casts they prepared for broken limbs. At one time, you could buy fine sculptures made of hashish, as well as oil paintings in which "stuff" was concealed. A list of such subterfuges would be endless. What is more, in Kandahar, you can even obtain the stuff at Government-run stores—in any quantity you wish.

The story is told of an American who loaded his Volkswagen bus with 200 kilos of hashish, an unbelievable amount. The fragrance alone sufficed to intoxicate him completely, and, as a result, he collided head-on with a truck (and there aren't too many trucks on the road in Afghanistan). They pulled him out from under his treasure, seriously injured, and eventually—this may seem incredible, considering the situation in Afghanistan—he was tried and convicted.

A good many of the guests in our little hotel tried to horn in on the smuggling game and came to grief. Just over the border, in Pakistan, is located one of the largest smuggling centers in the area, the village of Landi Kotal. From the highway, which passes over the clay roofs of the village, one can catch only a fleeting glimpse of the bazaar, which stands right beneath the road. Here, Pakistani soldiers and policemen try desperately to stop the smuggling. Many of Kabul's hippies used to buy a few kilos in this place (if they had the addresses and the confidence of the dealers) and would later sell them in Kabul. Nowadays, things are more risky. If your passport has more than three Afghan visas, they will search your baggage and search again, until they find what they expect to find. An unpleasant fate awaits him who is caught.

But all this hardly troubles the hotel guests. *Alice in Wonderland,* Huxley's new "doors of perception," and Baudelaire's *"paradis artificiels"* cause them to imagine themselves in a veritable paradise—a paradise, of course, which does not extend beyond the walls of the garden. With the help of prophetic quotations from the *I Ching,* China's most ancient philosophical treatise, they try to separate reason from unreason and the future from the present. They love to travel, and, if you ask them who they are or what they are, they will always describe themselves as "travelers" or *"voyageurs"*—in both a geographical sense and in an inner dimension.

It is hard for them to say what they want, and they do not engage at all in calm, matter-of-fact discussions. You can take them seriously only if and when you "travel" with them. They regard themselves proudly as a new élite. But they are not arrogant; rather they exhibit the naiveté and amazement of an "Alice" who has just seen something marvelous. "There are pills that make you tall, there are pills that make you small," they sing to themselves. Those are the opening lines of a typical hit song, performed by the "Jefferson Airplane," called "White Rabbit," after the mysterious rabbit in *Alice in Wonderland.*

Translated from the German

Leaf in the Wind

BERNARD B. DADIÉ

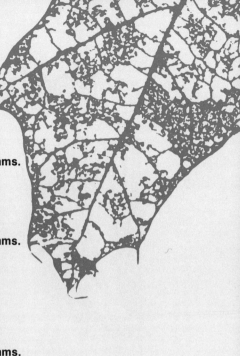

I am the man the color of Night

Leaf in the wind, I go at the drift of my dreams.

I am the tree putting forth shoots in spring
The dew that hums in the baobab's hollow.

Leaf in the wind, I go at the drift of my dreams.

I am the man they complain of
Because opposed to formality
The man they laugh at
Because opposed to barriers.

Leaf in the wind, I go at the drift of my dreams.

I am the man they talk about:
"Oh him!"
Him you cannot hold
The breeze that touches you and is gone

Leaf in the wind, I go at the drift of my dreams.

Captain at the stern
Scanning the scudding clouds
For the earth's powerful eye;
Ship without sail
That glides on the sea

Leaf in the wind, I go at the drift of my dreams.

I am the man whose dreams
Are manifold as the stars
More murmurous than swarms of bees
More smiling than children's smiles
More sonorous than echoes in the woods.

Leaf in the wind, I go at the drift of my dreams.

Translated from the French

Fool's Paradise

ISAAC BASHEVIS SINGER

Somewhere, sometime, there lived a rich man whose name was Kadish. He had an only son who was called Atzel. In the household of Kadish there lived a distant relative, an orphan girl, called Aksah. Atzel was a tall boy with black hair and black eyes. Aksah was somewhat shorter than Atzel, and she had blue eyes and golden hair. Both were about the same age. As children, they ate together, studied together, played together. Atzel played the husband; Aksah, his wife. It was taken for granted that when they grew up they would really marry.

But when they had grown up, Atzel suddenly became ill. It was a sickness no one had ever heard of before: Atzel imagined that he was dead.

How did such an idea come to him? It seems it came from listening to stories about paradise. He had had an old nurse who had constantly described the place to him. She had told him that in paradise it was not necessary to work or to study or make any effort whatsoever. In paradise one ate the meat of wild oxen and the flesh of whales; one drank the wine that the Lord reserved for the just; one slept late into the day; and one had no duties.

Atzel was lazy by nature. He hated to get up early in the morning and to study languages and science. He knew that one day he would have to take over his father's business and he did not want to.

Since his old nurse had told Atzel that the only way to get to paradise was to die, he had made up his mind to do just that as quickly as possible. He thought and brooded about it so much that soon he began to imagine that he *was* dead.

Of course his parents became terribly worried when they saw what was happening to Atzel. Aksah cried in secret. The family did everything possible to try to convince Atzel that he was alive, but he refused to believe them. He would say, "Why don't you bury me? You see that I am dead. Because of you I cannot get to paradise."

Many doctors were called in to examine Atzel, and all tried to convince the boy that he was alive. They pointed out that he was talking, eating, and sleeping. But before long Atzel began to eat less and he rarely spoke. His family feared that he would die.

In despair Kadish went to consult a great specialist, celebrated for his knowledge and wisdom. His name was Dr. Yoetz. After listening to a description of Atzel's illness, he said to Kadish, "I promise to cure your son in eight days, on one condition. You must do whatever I tell you to, no matter how strange it may seem."

Kadish agreed, and Dr. Yoetz said he would visit Atzel that same day. Kadish went home to prepare the household. He told his wife, Aksah, and the servants that all were to follow the doctor's orders without question, and they did so.

When Dr. Yoetz arrived, he was taken to Atzel's room. The boy lay on his bed, pale and thin from fasting, his hair disheveled, his nightclothes wrinkled.

The doctor took one look at Atzel and called out, "Why do you keep a dead body in the house? Why don't you make a funeral?"

On hearing these words the parents became terribly frightened, but Atzel's face lit up with a smile and he said, "You see, I was right."

Although Kadish and his wife were bewildered by the doctor's words, they remembered Kadish's promise, and went immediately to make arrangements for the funeral.

Atzel now became so excited by what the doctor had said that he jumped out of bed and began to dance and clap his hands. His joy made him hungry and he asked for food. But Dr. Yoetz replied, "Wait, you will eat in paradise."

The doctor requested that a room be prepared to look like paradise. The walls were hung with white satin, and precious rugs covered the floors. The windows were shuttered, and draperies tightly drawn. Candles and oil lamps burned day and night. The servants were dressed in white with wings on their backs and were to play angels.

Atzel was placed in an open coffin, and a funeral ceremony was held. Atzel was so exhausted with happiness that he slept right through it. When he awoke, he found himself in a room he didn't recognize. "Where am I?" he asked.

"In paradise, my lord," a winged servant replied.

"I'm terribly hungry," Atzel said. "I'd like some whale flesh and sacred wine."

"In a moment, my lord."

The chief servant clapped his hands and a door opened through which there came men servants and maids, all with wings on their backs, bearing golden trays laden with meat, fish, pomegranates and persimmons, pineapples and peaches. A tall servant with a long white beard carried a golden goblet full of wine. Atzel was so starved that he ate ravenously. The angels hovered around him, filling his plate and goblet even before he had time to ask for more.

When he had finished eating, Atzel declared he wanted to rest. Two angels undressed and bathed him. Then they brought him a nightdress of fine embroidered linen, placed a nightcap with a tassel on his head, and carried him to a bed with silken sheets and a purple velvet canopy. Atzel immediately fell into a deep and happy sleep.

When he awoke, it was morning but it could just as well have been night. The shutters were closed, and the candles and oil lamps were burning. As soon as the servants saw that Atzel was awake, they brought in exactly the same meal as the day before.

"Why do you give me the same food as yesterday?" Atzel asked. "Don't you have any milk, coffee, fresh rolls, and butter?"

"No, my lord. In paradise one always eats the same food," the servant replied.

"Is it already day, or is it still night?" Atzel asked.

"In paradise there is neither day nor night."

Dr. Yoetz had given careful instructions on how the servants were to talk to Atzel and behave toward him.

Atzel again ate the fish, meat, fruit, and drank the wine, but his appetite was not as good as it had been. When he had finished his meal and washed his hands in a golden finger bowl, he asked, "What time is it?"

"In paradise time does not exist," the servant answered.

"What shall I do now?" Atzel questioned.

"In paradise, my lord, one doesn't do anything."

"Where are the other saints?" Atzel inquired. "I'd like to meet them."

"In paradise each family has a place of its own."

"Can't one go visiting?"

"In paradise the dwellings are too far from each other for visiting. It would take thousands of years to go from one to the other."

"When will my family come?" Atzel asked.

"Your father still has twenty years to live, your mother thirty. And as long as they live they can't come here."

"What about Aksah?"

"She has more than fifty years to live."

"Do I have to be alone all that time?"

"Yes, my lord."

For a while Atzel shook his head, pondering. Then he asked, "What is Aksah going to do?"

"Right now, she's mourning for you. But you know, my lord, that one cannot mourn forever. Sooner or later she will forget you, meet another young man, and marry. That's how it is with the living."

Atzel got up and began to walk to and fro. His long sleep and the rich food had restored his energy. For the first time in years, lazy Atzel had a desire to do something, but there was nothing to do in his paradise.

For eight days Atzel remained in his false heaven, and from day to day he became sadder and sadder. He missed his father; he longed for his mother; he yearned for Aksah. Idleness did not appeal to him as it had in former times. Now he wished he had something to study; he dreamed of traveling; he wanted to ride his horse, to talk to friends. The food, which had so delighted him the first day, lost its flavor.

The time came when he could no longer conceal his sadness. He remarked to one of the servants, "I see now that it is not as bad to live as I had thought."

"To live, my lord, is difficult. One has to study, work, do business. Here everything is easy," the servant consoled him.

"I would rather chop wood and carry stones than sit here. And how long will this last?"

"Forever."

"Stay here forever?" Atzel began to tear his hair in grief. "I'd rather kill myself."

"A dead man cannot kill himself."

On the eighth day, when it seemed that Atzel had reached the deepest despair, one of the servants, as had been arranged, came to him and said, "My lord, there has been a mistake. You are not dead. You must leave paradise."

"I'm alive?"

"Yes, you are alive, and I will bring you back to earth."

Atzel was beside himself with joy. The servant blindfolded him, and after leading him back and forth through the long corridors of the house, brought him to the room where his family was waiting and uncovered his eyes.

It was a bright day, and the sun shone through the open windows. A breeze from the surrounding fields and orchards freshened the air. In the garden outside, the birds were singing and the bees buzzing as they flew from flower to flower. From the barns and stables Atzel could hear the mooing of cows and the neighing of horses. Joyfully he embraced and kissed his parents and Aksah.

"I didn't know how good it was to be alive," he cried out.

And to Aksah he said, "Haven't you met another young man while I was away? Do you still love me?"

"Yes, I do, Atzel. I could not forget you."

"If that is so, it is time we got married."

It was not long before the wedding took place. Dr. Yoetz was the guest of honor. Musicians played; guests came from faraway cities. Some came on horseback, some drove mules, and some rode camels. All brought fine gifts for the bride and groom, in gold, silver, ivory, and assorted precious stones. The celebration lasted seven days and seven nights. It was one of the gayest weddings that old men had ever remembered. Atzel and Aksah were extremely happy, and both lived to a ripe old age. Atzel stopped being lazy and became the most diligent merchant in the whole region. His trading caravans traveled as far as Baghdad and India.

It was not until after the wedding that Atzel learned how Dr. Yoetz had cured him, and that he had lived in a fool's paradise. In the years to come he often talked with Aksah about his adventures, and later they told the tale of Dr. Yoetz's wonderful cure to their children and grandchildren, always finishing with the words, "But, of course, what paradise is really like, no one can tell."

Love of One's Neighbor

LEONID ANDREYEV

Characters

FIRST POLICEMAN	ALEC
BOY	MARY
SECOND POLICEMAN	KATE
LADY	JIMMY
LITTLE GIRL	TALL TOURIST
VOICES	FIRST DRUNKEN MAN
FIRST ENGLISHMAN	SECOND DRUNKEN MAN
SECOND ENGLISHMAN	CORRESPONDENT
UNKNOWN MAN	FIRST TOURIST
QUIET TOURIST	SECOND TOURIST
MILITARY WOMAN	PASTOR
PHOTOGRAPHER	THE MAN IN THE WHITE VEST
LITTLE LADY	THE MAN CARRYING THE POLE
FAT TOURIST	

SCENE: *A wild place in the mountains. A man in an attitude of despair is standing on a tiny projection of rock that rises almost sheer from the ground. How he got there it is not easy to say, but he cannot be reached either from above or below. Short ladders, ropes, and sticks show that attempts have been made to save the unknown person, but without success.*

It seems that the man has been in that position a long time. A considerable crowd has already collected, extremely varied in composition. There are vendors of cold drinks; there is a whole little bar behind which the bartender skips about, out of breath and perspiring—he has more on his hands than he can attend to; there are peddlers selling picture post cards, coral beads, souvenirs, and all sorts of trash. Tourists keep pouring in from all sides. Nearly all carry alpenstocks, field glasses, and cameras.

At the foot of the rock where the unknown man is to fall, two policemen are chasing the children away and partitioning off a space, drawing a rope around short stakes stuck in the ground. It is noisy and jolly.

FIRST POLICEMAN. Get away, you loafer! The man'll fall on your head and then your mother and father will be making a hullabaloo about it.

BOY. Will he fall here?

POLICEMAN. Yes, here.

BOY. Suppose he drops farther off?

SECOND POLICEMAN. The boy is right. He may get desperate and jump, land beyond the rope, and hit some people in the crowd. I'd guess he weighs at least two hundred pounds.

178

FIRST POLICEMAN. Move on, move on, you! Where are you going? Is that your daughter, lady? Please take her away! The young man will soon fall.

LADY. Soon? Did you say he is going to fall soon? Oh, heavens, and my husband's not here!

LITTLE GIRL. He's in the café, Mama.

LADY (*desperately*). Yes, of course. He's always in the café. Go call him, Nellie. Tell him the man will soon drop. Hurry! Hurry!

VOICES. Waiter! Three beers out here! No beer? What? Say, that's a fine bar! Waiter! Waiter!

FIRST POLICEMAN. Say, boy, you here again?

BOY. I wanted to take the stone away.

POLICEMAN. What for?

BOY. So he won't get hurt so badly when he falls.

SECOND POLICEMAN. The boy is right. We ought to remove the stone. We ought to clear the place altogether. Isn't there any sawdust or sand about?

(*Two* ENGLISHMEN *enter. They look at the unknown man through field glasses.*)

FIRST ENGLISHMAN (*to the* FIRST POLICEMAN). How did he get up there? Why don't they take him off?

POLICEMAN. They tried, but they couldn't. Our ladders are too short.

SECOND ENGLISHMAN. Has he been there long?

POLICEMAN. Two days.

FIRST ENGLISHMAN. Aha! He'll drop at night.

SECOND ENGLISHMAN. In two hours, I'll bet a hundred to a hundred.

FIRST ENGLISHMAN. Put it down. (*He shouts to the man on the rock.*) How are you feeling? What? I can't hear you.

UNKNOWN MAN (*in a scarcely audible voice*). Bad, very bad.

LADY. Oh, heavens, and my husband is not here!

LITTLE GIRL (*running in*). Papa said he'll get here in plenty of time. He's playing chess.

LADY. Oh, heavens! Nellie, tell him he must come. I insist. Will he fall soon, Mr. Policeman? No? Nellie, you go. I'll stay here and keep the place for Papa.

(*A tall, lanky woman of unusually independent and military appearance and a tourist dispute for the same place. The* TOURIST, *a short, quiet, rather weak man, feebly defends his rights; the* MILITARY WOMAN *is resolute and aggressive.*)

QUIET TOURIST. But, lady, it's my place. I've been standing here for two hours.

MILITARY WOMAN. What do I care how long you've been standing here?

I want this place. It offers a good view, and that's just what I want. Do you understand?

QUIET TOURIST (*weakly*). It's what I want, too.

MILITARY WOMAN. I beg your pardon, what do you know about these things anyway? Did you ever see a tiger tear a woman to pieces in a zoo, right before your eyes? Eh? What? Yes, exactly. Well, I did. Now, please!

(*The* QUIET TOURIST *steps aside, shrugging his shoulders with an air of injury, and the tall woman triumphantly takes possession of the stone she has won by her prowess. She sits down, spreads out her bag, handkerchief, peppermints, and medicine bottle, takes off her gloves, and wipes her field glasses, glancing pleasantly on all around. Finally she turns to the* LADY *who is waiting for her husband.*)

MILITARY WOMAN. Men are so rude nowadays. They will never give their place to a woman. Have you brought peppermints with you?

LADY (*frightened*). No. Why? Is it necessary?

MILITARY WOMAN. When you keep looking up for a long time you are bound to get sick. Sure thing! Have you any spirits of ammonia? No? Good gracious, how thoughtless! How will they bring you back to consciousness when he falls? Have you anybody to take care of you, seeing that you are so helpless yourself?

LADY (*frightened*). I'll tell my husband. He's in the café.

MILITARY WOMAN. Your husband is a brute.

SECOND POLICEMAN. Whose coat is this? Who threw this rag here?

BOY. It's mine. I spread my coat there so that he won't hurt himself so badly when he falls.

POLICEMAN. Take it away.

PHOTOGRAPHER. For heaven's sake, lady, you're sitting on my camera!

LITTLE LADY. Oh! Where is it?

PHOTOGRAPHER. Under you, under you, lady.

LITTLE LADY. I am so tired. What a wretched camera you have. I thought it felt uncomfortable and I was wondering why. Now I know; I am sitting on your camera.

PHOTOGRAPHER (*agonized*). Lady, for heaven's sake!

LITTLE LADY. Why is it so large, tell me? Cameras are small, but this one is so large. I swear I never had the faintest suspicion it was a camera. Can you take my picture? I would so much like to have my picture taken in this wonderful setting.

PHOTOGRAPHER. How can I take your picture if you are sitting on my camera?

LITTLE LADY (*jumping up, frightened*). Is it possible? You don't say so! Why didn't you tell me? Does it take pictures?

(*A* FAT TOURIST *enters in hast, panting, surrounded by a large family.*)

FAT TOURIST (*crying*). Mary! Alec! Kate! Jimmy! Where is Mary? For heaven's sake! Where is Mary?

ALEC (*dismally*). Here she is, Papa.

FAT TOURIST. Where is she? Mary!

MARY. Here I am, Papa.

FAT TOURIST. Where in the world are you? (*He turns around.*) Ah, there! What are you standing back of me for? Look, look! For goodness sake, where are you looking?

MARY (*dismally*). I don't know, Papa.

FAT TOURIST. No, that's impossible. Imagine! She never once saw a lightning flash. She always keeps her eyes open as wide as onions, but the instant it flashes she closes them. So she never saw lightning, not once. Mary, you are missing it again. There it is! See!

ALEC. She sees, Papa.

FAT TOURIST. Keep an eye on her. (*Suddenly dropping into tone of profound pity*) Ah, poor young man. Imagine! He'll fall from that high rock. Look, children. That should be a lesson to you how dangerous climbing is.

ALEC (*dismally*). He won't fall today, Papa!

KATE. Papa, Mary has closed her eyes again.

ALEC. Let us sit down, Papa! Upon my word, he won't fall today. The porter told me so. I can't stand it any more. You've been dragging us around every day from morning till night visiting art galleries.

FAT TOURIST. What's that? For whose benefit am I doing this?

KATE. Papa, Mary is blinking her eyes.

JIMMY. I can't stand it, either. I have terrible dreams.

ALEC. I have gotten so thin I am nothing but skin and bones. I can't stand it any more, Father. I'd rather be a farmer, or tend pigs.

FAT TOURIST. Alec.

ALEC. If he were really to fall—but it's a fake. You believe every lie that's told you! They all lie.

MARY (*dismally*). Papa, children, he's beginning to fall.

(*The man on the rock shouts something down into the crowd. There is a general commotion. Voices: "Look, he's falling." Field glasses are raised; the* PHOTOGRAPHER, *violently agitated, clicks his camera; the* POLICEMEN *diligently clean the place where he is to fall.*)

VOICES. Hush! He's getting ready to fall. No, he's saying something. No, he's falling. Hush!

UNKNOWN MAN (*faintly*). Save me! Save me!

FAT TOURIST. Ah, poor young man. Mary, Jimmy, there's a tragedy for you. The sky is clear, the weather is beautiful, and he has to fall and be shattered to death! Can you realize how dreadful that is, Alec?

181

ALEC (*wearily*). Yes, I can realize it.

FAT TOURIST. Mary, can you realize it? Imagine. There is the sky. There are people enjoying themselves and partaking of refreshments. Everything is so nice and pleasant, and he has to fall. What a tragedy!

ALEC. Why don't you order sandwiches, Father?

MILITARY WOMAN (*amiably*). Are all these your children?

FAT TOURIST. Yes, madam. A father's duty. You see, they are protesting. It is the eternal conflict between fathers and children. Here is such a tragedy going on, such a heart-rending tragedy—Mary, you are blinking your eyes again.

MILITARY WOMAN. You are quite right. Children must be hardened to things. But why do you call this a terrible tragedy? Every roofer, when he falls, falls from a great height. But this here—what is it? A hundred, two hundred feet. I saw a man fall plumb from the sky.

FAT TOURIST. How terrible!

MILITARY WOMAN. That's what I call a tragedy. It took two hours to bring me back to consciousness. From that day on I never step out of the door without taking spirits of ammonia with me.

(TALL TOURIST, *with upcurled mustache, violently gesticulating, enters, followed by a small group attracted by curiosity.*)

TALL TOURIST. It's scandalous. Why don't they save him? Ladies and gentlemen, you all heard him shout, "Save me." Didn't you all hear him?

VOICES (*in chorus*). Yes, yes, we heard him.

TALL TOURIST. There you are. I distinctly heard these words: "Save me! Why don't they save me?" It's scandalous. Policemen, policemen! Why don't you save him? What are you doing there?

POLICEMEN. We are cleaning up the place for him to fall.

TALL TOURIST. That's a sensible thing to do, too. But why don't you save him? You ought to save him. If a man asks you to save him, it is absolutely essential to save him. Isn't that so, ladies and gentlemen?

VOICES (*in chorus*). True, absolutely true.

TALL TOURIST (*with heat*). We are not heathens; we are Christians. We should love our neighbors. When a man asks to be saved, every measure which the government has at its command should be taken to save him. Policemen, have you taken every measure?

POLICEMEN. Every one!

TALL TOURIST. Every one without exception? Listen, young man, every measure has been taken to save you.

UNKNOWN MAN (*in a scarcely audible voice*). Save me!

TALL TOURIST. Didn't I say so? Of course, we must put in a complaint. Young man! Listen, young man. Do you pay taxes? What? I can't hear.

FAT TOURIST. Jimmy, Katie, listen! What a tragedy! Ah, the poor young man! He is soon to fall and they ask him to pay a tax.

TALL TOURIST. We must hurry, ladies and gentlemen. He must be saved at any cost. Who's going with me?

VOICES (*in chorus*). We are all going!

TALL TOURIST. Come, ladies and gentlemen!

(*They depart, fiercely gesticulating. The café grows more lively. The bartender wipes the perspiration from his face with his napkin. Angry calls of "Waiter! Waiter!"*)

UNKNOWN MAN (*rather loudly*). Can you let me have some soda water?

(*The* WAITER *is startled, looks at the sky, glances at the man on the rock, and, pretending not to have heard him, walks away.*)

MANY VOICES. Waiter! Beer!

(*Two* DRUNKEN MEN *come out from the café.*)

LADY. Ah, there is my husband.

MILITARY WOMAN. A downright brute.

FIRST DRUNKEN MAN (*waving his hand to the* UNKNOWN MAN). Say, is it very bad up there? Hey?

UNKNOWN MAN (*rather loudly*). Yes, it's bad. I am sick and tired of it.

FIRST DRUNKEN MAN. Can't you get a drink?

UNKNOWN MAN. No, how can I?

SECOND DRUNKEN MAN. Say, what are you talking about? How can he get a drink? The man is about to die and you tempt him and try to get him excited. Listen, up there. We have been drinking your health.

FIRST DRUNKEN MAN. What are you talking about? How can it hurt him? Why, it will only do him good. It will encourage him. Listen, honest. We are very very sorry for you, but don't mind us. We are going to the café to have another drink.

(*Enter a new crowd of tourists, with a very elegant gentleman, the chief correspondent of the European newspapers, at their head. He is followed by an ecstatic whisper of respect and admiration.*)

VOICES. The correspondent! The correspondent! Look!

LADY. Oh, my, and my husband is gone again!

FAT TOURIST. Jimmy, Mary, Alec, Katie, look! This is the chief correspondent. Do you realize it? The very highest of all. Whatever he writes goes.

KATE. Mary, dear, you are not looking again.

ALEC. I wish you would order some sandwiches for us. I can't stand it any longer. A human being has to eat.

FAT TOURIST (*ecstatically*). What a tragedy! Katie, dear, can you realize it? The weather is so beautiful, and the chief correspondent! Take out your notebook, Jimmy.

JIMMY. I lost it, Father.

CORRESPONDENT. Where is he?

VOICES (*obligingly*). There, there he is. There! A little higher. Still higher! A little lower! No, higher!

CORRESPONDENT. If you please, if you please, ladies and gentlemen, I will find him myself. Oh, yes, there he is. Mm! What a situation! Very interesting, indeed! (*Whisks out his notebook; nods amiably to photographer*) Have you taken any pictures yet, sir?

PHOTOGRAPHER. Yes, sir, certainly, certainly. I have photographed the place, showing the general character of the locality——

CORRESPONDENT. Ye-es, very, very interesting.

FAT TOURIST. Did you hear, Alec? This smart man, the chief correspondent, says it's interesting, and you keep bothering about sandwiches.

ALEC. Maybe he's had his dinner already.

CORRESPONDENT (*shouts to the* UNKNOWN MAN). Permit me to introduce myself. I am the chief correspondent of the European press. I have been sent here at the special request of the editors. I should like to ask you several questions concerning your situation. What is your name? Are you married? How old are you?

(*The* UNKNOWN MAN *mumbles something.*)

CORRESPONDENT (*a little puzzled*). I can't hear a thing. Has he been that way all the time?

PHOTOGRAPHER. Yes, it's impossible to hear a word he says.

CORRESPONDENT. I can't hear you. Are you married? Yes?

FIRST TOURIST. He said he was a bachelor.

SECOND TOURIST. No, he didn't. Of course he's married.

CORRESPONDENT (*carelessly*). You think so? All right. We'll put down "married." How many children have you? Can't hear. It seems to me he said three. Hm! Anyway, we'll put down five.

FIRST TOURIST. Oh, my, what a tragedy. Five children! Imagine!

MILITARY WOMAN. He's lying.

CORRESPONDENT (*shouting*). How did you get into this position? What? I can't hear! Louder! Repeat. What did you say? (*Perplexed, to the crowd*) What did he say? The fellow has a devilishly weak voice.

FIRST TOURIST. It seems to me he said that he lost his way.

SECOND TOURIST. No, he doesn't know himself how he got there.

VOICES. He was out hunting. He was climbing up the rocks. No, no! He is simply a lunatic!

CORRESPONDENT (*writing in his notebook*). Unhappy young man—suffering from childhood with attacks of lunacy. The bright light of the full moon—the wild rocks, didn't notice——

FIRST TOURIST (*to the* SECOND, *in a whisper*). But it's a new moon now.

SECOND TOURIST. Go on, what does a layman know about astronomy?

FAT TOURIST (*ecstatically*). Mary, pay attention to this! You have before you an ocular demonstration of the influence of the moon on living organisms. What a terrible tragedy to go out walking on a moonlit night and find suddenly that you have climbed to a place where it is impossible to climb down or be taken down.

CORRESPONDENT (*shouting*). What feelings are you experiencing? I can't hear. Louder! Ah, so, well, well! What a situation!

VOICES (*interested*). Listen, listen! Let's hear what his feelings are. How terrible!

CORRESPONDENT (*writes in his notebook, tossing out detached remarks*). Mortal terror numbs his limbs—A cold shiver goes down his spinal column—No hope—Before his mental vision rises a picture of family bliss: wife making sandwiches; his five children innocently lisping their love. Deeply moved by the sympathy of the public—His last wish before his death that the words he uttered with his last breath should be published in our newspapers—

MILITARY WOMAN (*indignantly*). My! He lies like a salesman.

CORRESPONDENT (*shouting*). Hold on fast. That's it. My last question: What message do you wish to leave for your fellow citizens before you depart for the better world?

UNKNOWN MAN. That they may all go to the devil.

CORRESPONDENT. What? Hm, yes. (*He writes quickly.*) Ardent love—is a staunch supporter of all laws granting equal rights to minority groups. His last words: "Let them all——"

PASTOR (*out of breath, pushing through the crowd*). Where is he? Ah, where is he? Ah, there! Poor young man. Has there been no clergyman here yet? No? Thank you. Am I the first?

CORRESPONDENT (*writes*). A touching dramatic moment. A minister has arrived. All are trembling on the verge of suspense.

185

FIRST ENGLISHMAN. Listen, won't you hurry up and fall?

SECOND ENGLISHMAN. What are you saying, Sir William?

FIRST ENGLISHMAN (*shouting*). Don't you see that's what they are waiting for? As a gentleman, you should grant them this pleasure!

SECOND ENGLISHMAN. Sir William . . .

FIRST TOURIST (*going for the* FIRST ENGLISHMAN). How dare you?

FIRST ENGLISHMAN (*shoving him aside*). Hurry up and fall! Do you hear? If you haven't the backbone, I'll help you out with a pistol shot.

SECOND TOURIST. That red-haired devil has gone clear out of his mind.

POLICEMAN (*seizing the* ENGLISHMAN'*s hand*). You have no right to do it; it's against the law. I'll arrest you.

UNKNOWN MAN (*aloud*). Take that idiot away to the devil. He wants to shoot me. And tell the boss that I can't stand it any longer.

VOICES. What's that? What boss? He is losing his mind, the poor man.

UNKNOWN MAN (*angrily*). Tell him my spinal column is broken.

MARY (*wearily*). Papa, children, he's beginning to kick with his legs.

KATE. Is that what is called convulsions, Papa?

FAT TOURIST (*rapturously*). I don't know. I think it is. What a tragedy.

ALEC (*to* KATE). You fool! You keep studying and studying and you don't know that the right name for that is agony. And you wear eyeglasses, too. I can't bear it any longer, Papa.

FAT TOURIST. Think of it, children. A man is about to fall down to his death and he is bothering about his spinal column!

(*There is a noise. A* MAN IN A WHITE VEST, *very much frightened, enters, almost dragged by angry tourists.*)

VOICES. A barefaced deception! It is an outrage. Policeman, policeman, he must be taught a lesson!

MORE VOICES. What is it? What deception? What is it all about? They have caught a thief!

UNKNOWN MAN. The agreement was till twelve o'clock. What time is it now?

TALL TOURIST (*indignantly*). Do you hear, ladies and gentlemen? This scoundrel, this man here in the white vest, hired that other scoundrel up there and just simply tied him to the rock.

VOICES. Is he tied?

TALL TOURIST. Yes, he is tied and he can't fall. Here we are, all excited and worrying, and he couldn't fall even if he tried.

UNKNOWN MAN. What else do you want? Do you think I am going to break my neck for your measly ten dollars? Boss, I can't stand it any more. One man wanted to shoot me. This was not in the agreement. Another wanted to preach at me.

ALEC. Father, I told you. You believe everything anybody tells you and drag us about without eating.

WHITE VEST. The people were bored. My only desire was to amuse the people.

MILITARY WOMAN. What's the matter? I don't understand a thing. Why isn't he going to fall?

FAT TOURIST. I don't understand a thing either. He's got to fall!

JIMMY. You never understand anything, Father. Weren't you told that he's tied to the rock?

ALEC. You can't convince him.

FAT TOURIST. Silence!

TALL TOURIST. The idea! What a deception! You'll have to explain.

WHITE VEST. The people were bored. Excuse me, ladies and gentlemen, but wishing to accommodate you—give you a few hours of pleasant excitement—inspire you with altruistic sentiments——

FIRST ENGLISHMAN. Is the café yours?

WHITE VEST. Yes.

FIRST ENGLISHMAN. And is the hotel ·below also yours?

WHITE VEST. Yes. The people were bored——

CORRESPONDENT (*writing*). The proprietor of the café, desiring to increase his profits from the sale of alcoholic beverages, exploits the best human sentiments. The people's indignation——

UNKNOWN MAN (*angrily*). Boss, will you have me taken off at once or won't you?

WHITE VEST. What do you want up there? Aren't you satisfied? Didn't I have you taken off at night?

UNKNOWN MAN. Well, I should say so. You think I'd be hanging here nights, too?

WHITE VEST. Then you can stand it a few minutes longer.

TALL TOURIST. Say, have you any idea what you've done? You are scoundrels, who for your own sordid personal ends have impiously exploited the finest human sentiment, love of one's neighbor. You have caused us to undergo fear and suffering. You have poisoned our hearts with pity. And now, what is the upshot of it all? The upshot is that this scamp, your vile accomplice, is bound to the rock and not only will he not fall, as everybody expected, but he can't.

FAT TOURIST. Policeman! You must draw up an official report.

MILITARY WOMAN (*going for the* MAN IN WHITE VEST). I will not allow myself to be fooled. I saw a plane drop from the clouds and go crash upon a roof. I saw a tiger tear a woman to pieces——

PHOTOGRAPHER. I spoiled three films photographing that scamp. You will have to answer for this, sir.

FAT TOURIST. An official report! An official report! Such a barefaced deception. Mary, Jimmy, Alec, call a policeman.

WHITE VEST (*drawing back, in despair*). But, I can't make him fall if he doesn't want to. I did everything in my power. I promise you on my word of honor that the next time he will fall. But he doesn't want to, today.

UNKNOWN MAN. What's that? What did you say about the next time?

WHITE VEST. You shut up there!

UNKNOWN MAN. For ten dollars?

MARY (*wearily*). Papa, children, look! A policeman is coming.

POLICEMAN. Excuse me, excuse me, ladies and gentlemen.

WHITE VEST. I can't make him fall if he doesn't want to.

POLICEMAN. Hey, you, young man up there! Can you fall or can't you? Confess!

UNKNOWN MAN (*sullenly*). I don't want to fall!

VOICES. Aha, he has confessed. What a scoundrel!

TALL TOURIST. Write down what I dictate, policeman. "Desiring, for the sake of gain, to exploit the sentiment of love of one's neighbor—the sacred feeling which—a—a——"

FAT TOURIST. Listen, children, they are drawing up an official report. What exquisite choice of language!

POLICEMAN (*writing with painful effort, his tongue stuck out*). ". . . love of one's neighbor—the sacred feeling which——"

MARY (*wearily*). Papa, children, look! An advertisement is coming.

(*Enter musicians with trumpets and drums, a man at their head carrying on a long pole a huge placard with the picture of an absolutely bald head, and printed underneath: "I Was Bald."*)

MAN CARRYING POLE (*stopping and speaking in a loud voice*). I had been bald from the day of my birth and for a long time thereafter. That miserable growth, which in my tenth year covered my scalp, was more like rope than real hair. When I was married, my skull was as bare as a pillow, and my young bride——

FAT TOURIST. What a tragedy! Newly married and with such a head! Can you realize how dreadful that is, children?

(*All listen with interest; even the* POLICEMAN *stops his arduous task and inclines his ear, with his pen poised.*)

MAN CARRYING POLE (*solemnly*). And the time came when my matrimonial happiness literally hung by a hair. All the medicines recommended by quacks to make my hair grow——

FAT TOURIST. Your notebook, Jimmy.

MILITARY WOMAN. But when is he going to fall?

WHITE VEST (*amiably*). The next time, lady. I won't tie him so tight—you understand?

Translated by Thomas Seltzer

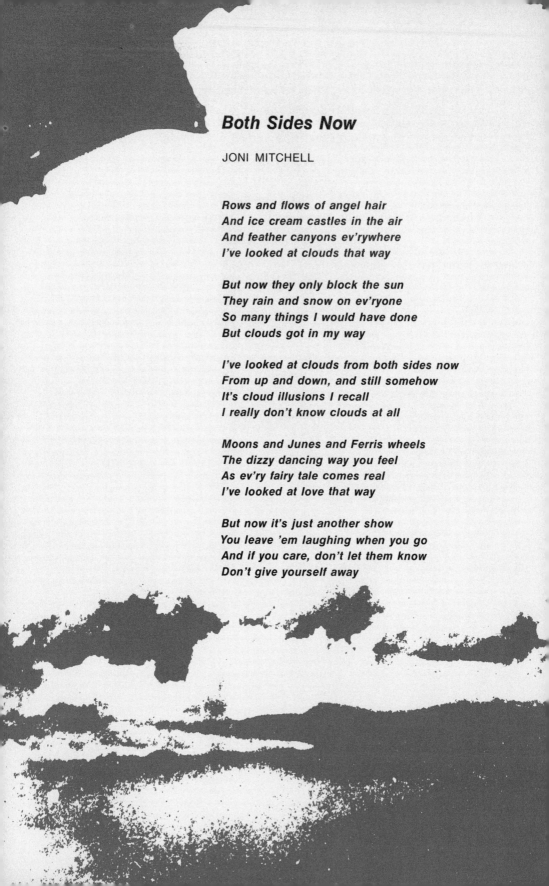

Both Sides Now

JONI MITCHELL

*Rows and flows of angel hair
And ice cream castles in the air
And feather canyons ev'rywhere
I've looked at clouds that way*

*But now they only block the sun
They rain and snow on ev'ryone
So many things I would have done
But clouds got in my way*

*I've looked at clouds from both sides now
From up and down, and still somehow
It's cloud illusions I recall
I really don't know clouds at all*

*Moons and Junes and Ferris wheels
The dizzy dancing way you feel
As ev'ry fairy tale comes real
I've looked at love that way*

*But now it's just another show
You leave 'em laughing when you go
And if you care, don't let them know
Don't give yourself away*

I've looked at love from both sides now
From give and take, and still somehow
It's love's illusions I recall
I really don't know love at all

Tears and fears and feeling proud
To say "I love you" right out loud
Dreams and schemes and circus crowds
I've looked at life that way

But now old friends are acting strange
They shake their heads, they say I've changed
But something's lost, but something's gained
In living ev'ry day

I've looked at life from both sides now
From win and lose and still somehow
It's life's illusions I recall
I really don't know life at all

1.

2.

3.

4.

5.

T.S.

Do what you've never done before

Do what you've never done before,
See what you've never seen,
Feel what you've never felt before,
Say what you've never said,
Bear what you've never borne before,
Hear what you've never heard.
All is not what it would seem;
Nothing ever remains the same.
Change is life's characteristic;
Bend and flow and play the game. . . .
So many times I was the one
Who stopped myself from doing things;
So many times I was the one
Why grounded myself and clipped my wings.
So I say do what you've never done before. . . .
You must go where you have never been. . . .

From "New Year's Resovolution"
by Donovan Leitch (Ireland).

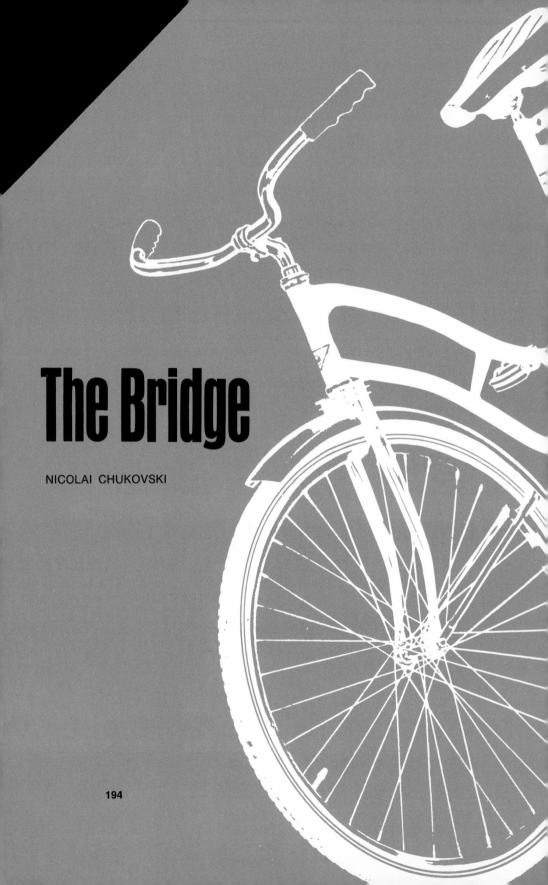

The Bridge

NICOLAI CHUKOVSKI

"I just can't see him going," Gramma said, turning over the potato cake in the pan with a knife. "He's scared of everything."

"He'll go," Aunt Nadya replied from the depths of the kitchen. "He has to go. He'll be better off there."

Gramma sighed loudly. She wasn't at all convinced Kostya would be better off there.

Kostya had heard every word. He stood not far from the open window amid the currant shrubs, quickly picking the berries and shoving them into his mouth. Since it had been decided he would have to go away, Kostya was spending hours at a time in these shrubs, their luxurious, end-of-July growth serving as an excellent hiding place. He liked to be alone and not have to talk to anyone. Through the branches creeping over the window sill into the shade-filled kitchen, he could see Gramma's hands moving over the kerosene burner, and hear the sizzling of the frying pancakes.

"He's scared of everything . . . everything," Gramma repeated. "He's afraid to buy a stamp in the post office. How'll he go?"

Kostya's mouth was getting sour from the berries. He worked his way out of the shrubbery, found his bicycle on the dark porch, and opened the kitchen door. Aunt Nadya was peeling potatoes—since it was Sunday she hadn't gone to work in the factory but was helping Gramma. The peels coiled like spirals over Aunt Nadya's thick, manlike fingers. Gramma, a squat, little woman, had just turned over another sizzling pancake. She looked up at the boy. Kostya knew that the mountain of potato cakes piled up in a plate at the burner was being baked for him—one more sign that his going away was final.

"I'm going for a little ride," he said glumly, hoisting the small bicycle over his shoulder.

Gramma sighed, stepping heavily from foot to foot. "Go on; have your last ride," Aunt Nadya told him without lifting her face from the potatoes. "You won't be doing it there."

Kostya walked the bicycle through the open wicket and threw his long leg over the frame. The bike, a juvenile size bought a long time ago, had become too small for him. This year he had shot up to almost twice his previous height, though otherwise he remained the same: narrow shoulders, a thin neck with a protruding Adam's apple, and slightly protuberant, translucent ears.

Mechanically Kostya rode out into the alley, hedged by dusty elder thickets. His sharp knees almost touched his chin, but he didn't mind—he was much too used to it. Mechanically he swerved to his left to cut into the open fields; he didn't want to meet anybody and didn't want anybody to disturb his thoughts.

Last spring after he was graduated from high school, barely getting promoted, Kostya had decided that going to the institute was out of the question. There had been a time his marks were no worse than anybody else's, but after his mother had died, a year and a half ago, he hadn't attended school for several months, and he had fallen too far behind to catch up. Everybody in class had known that Kostya never learned his lessons. He had become shy and unsure of himself, and the shyness had compounded his confusion whenever he'd been called to the blackboard.

And then his awkwardness. In company he'd either keep quiet or blurt out anything that came to his mind, then feel ashamed of himself. He had begun to avoid people, went swimming by himself, had even given up the soccer team. Once he had been shortchanged in the bakery shop and instead of reminding the saleswoman that she had made a mistake, he had told his grandmother that he had lost the money. Gramma was the only one with whom he felt at ease, unafraid. But now he'd have to leave her. . . .

This was the third year Gramma hadn't worked in the factory but had lived on her pension. Aunt Nadya had four little children; her husband had gone into construction work somewhere on the Volga, and there were rumors he had himself another woman—for the last year he hadn't sent home a kopeck. The whole settlement where Kostya had been born and lived all his starless seventeen years was made up of people working in the factory. It was a women's factory where a true man wouldn't be caught working.

Lads would leave the settlement as soon as they were graduated, and Kostya, too, would have to leave and stop living at Gramma's and Aunt Nadya's expense. But where? Uncle Vassily Petrovitch, Gramma's brother, had asked him to come, promising Gramma to take good care of him and find him a job. Everybody had thought that this was good and right, that a bright future was ahead of him . . . everybody but Kostya. Deep inside he was afraid nothing would come out of it; yet he didn't dare tell anybody.

He didn't dare confess to anybody how frightening was the thought of leaving Gramma. Uncle Vassily Petrovitch loomed in Kostya's mind like a cold, strict, old man of whom even Gramma was afraid. Quite often she had warned him "not to do anything to spite your uncle." Uncle Vasya had left for Siberia many years ago, before Kostya was even born, when his mother was still a little girl. He had been a tugboat captain on that great Siberian river that flows into the Arctic Ocean, but now he was more than that—he was a chief over a whole fleet of boats. Kostya often saw this river on a large map hanging in the classroom; with all its winding tributaries it reminded him of some strange plant with many weird roots stretching and stretching. . . .

Uncle Vasya often asked that Kostya come. "I'll enter him in the River Technicum together with my son Kolya," he wrote. "They will drill them there so that in three years both of them will become fine navigators."

When Gramma had read that letter she flinched and cast Kostya a frightened look at the word *drill*. And yet tonight they would go to the railroad station and wait for the Moscow train arriving at five in the morning. He would leave all by himself for Moscow, the unfamiliar, big city he had never seen before, and in Moscow he'd have to find his way to another railroad station, board another train leaving for Siberia, and he'd be all by himself with nothing to remind him of Gramma's comfort apart from the potato pancakes in the basket.

It was a warm but sunless, overcast day. Kostya rode out of the settlement and turned onto the highway running amid wavy fields. To the right, about three kilometers away, stretched the river—wide at times, hiding at times behind soft hills. The cloud-covered sky seemed to be hanging low over the usually busy highway, now deserted because it was Sunday. A warm, hay-scented breeze caressed the boy's face, as though careful not to disturb his thinking.

Deep in his thoughts, Kostya pushed the pedals, unaware of a little bird that kept perching on a telegraph post ahead of him, swinging its long tail, and seeming to wait until he caught up with it, then flying up again, perching on another post, farther away, and waiting again. The boy did not notice it, nor the old, thick-leaved linden trees—the remnants of an old road on which this highway was constructed—shooting up here and there like petrified explosions. Kostya pedaled onward where the gray ribbon of the macadam ran into the sunless twilight, rising softly or sloping gently.

Each time Kostya reached a crest of the wavy road, he had an excellent view to the next crest. Each time he was on the top of a hill he could see a green depression through which the road made a straight cut, first running down then up toward the crest where it butted against the sky and disappeared.

Hurdling one of these crests, Kostya sighted in the distance a minute, colored dot moving in the same direction. It occurred to him he might have noticed it before but had paid it no attention. There might have been a two-kilometer span between them—he only had a glimpse of it, looming blue and yellow, before it reached the next crest and vanished.

Kostya began to pedal faster. He dashed downhill, bouncing over a little bridge that spanned the two banks of a gully, then climbed the uphill stretch, using the impetus gained from the down-drive. He hurdled the crest and saw again the yellow-blue dot—bigger now, just beginning to move up the next rise. The distance between them had been shortened considerably; he could see it was somebody on a bicycle. How odd, he thought, so gaily dressed, yellow on top, blue below. Quite intrigued, Kostya leaned forward, pumping harder and harder, trying for greater speed.

As soon as he came over the next crest, he realized that the cyclist ahead of him was a girl wearing a blue skirt and yellow blouse, her fair hair falling down her back. She had been pedaling unhurriedly until she heard him coming from behind. As she turned her face to him, the glimpse Kostya caught was brief—a round, babyish face. There were still about two hundred meters separating them, and when she turned away again, her plump, little calves in the white socks began to push harder—the girl didn't want to be outdistanced.

She spurted ahead. Kostya leaned forward on the bars, pumping with all his might. Yet he was unable to cut the distance by much—she seemed to be quite good. On the next rise he appeared to gain a little, but when they came down the slope and the bikes rolled on their own, he stayed back somewhat. Her bike's better than mine, he thought. Yet the excitement of the chase added will to his strength. On the next rise he gained considerably, and covered the next downhill stretch, long as it was, without giving in a meter. Now he could see her well—no more than thirteen or fourteen. At times the girl turned her head slightly, seeming to try to catch a glimpse of him from the corner of her eye. Then he saw her chubby cheek, and a moment later he'd see her trying desperately to keep him from catching up with her. But he was drawing inexorably closer.

The girl's hair fluttered in the wind, exposing the back of her neck. They sped out of the fields, plunging into a forest of aspen, spruce and birch trees that seemed to rise into a solid wall. As the distance between the bicycles stubbornly decreased, Kostya was overcome by a sense of triumph. The girl's glances were more frequent, every time she tried to have a look at him, her bike made a little zig-zag, and he gained a few meters. He was sure now to catch up with her, probably on the next rise.

A recently laid asphalt road turned off the highway into the forest, right at the start of the rise. Kostya knew where it led—toward the river where a new bridge was being built to connect the state farms on both sides. But what he did not suspect was that the pursued bicycle would turn off to that road.

The girl made the turn abruptly. It was so sudden that he almost flashed by. She might have thought he would follow the highway and stop pursuing her. But Kostya had become so intensely elated that all he could think of now was catching up with her. He, too, swerved from the highway and spurted after her.

The road was downhill all the way. Both bicycles were tearing down at their maximum speeds, the girl steadily about ten meters ahead of Kostya. But he didn't care anymore—the road only led to the bridge now under construction and she'd have no choice but to stop there.

The road approached the bridge at an angle; through the tree trunks at the right the mirror of the river flashed far below under its steep bank. Cement barrels, sifters, and wooden scaffolding loomed before their eyes together with piles upon piles of scrap concrete—the unfinished structure was right in front of them.

The bridgework had no top layer yet, but it spanned both banks. It looked like a net scaled by a formless hodge-podge of wood in which the future metallic slickness could only be vaguely surmised. Now because it was Sunday, instead of the unceasing hum of work, a deep silence stood over the river.

Everything happened so fast that Kostya had no time to consider the danger. Suddenly he saw that the asphalt was coming to an end, and a four-plank trestle, laid over a sand embankment, led to the bridge. The girl pedaled ahead at top speed. Kostya was so shocked that before he had time to recover his wits he found himself, too, bouncing along those planks. He gripped the bar firmly to avoid veering off onto the sand. But the sand wasn't what bothered him. What frightened him was the realization that the trestle ran from the embankment onto the truss, across the unfenced iron girders which served as a narrow path for the bridge workers—high above the water. Was she insane? She was coming to the end of the embankment without slowing down!

"Brake! Brake!" he managed to shout out. But then he choked on his own words.

The girl half-turned at the sound of his voice. Again she glanced at him from the corner of one eye. Her bicycle, making a slight zig-zag almost pulled her off the planks. But she managed to straighten out the wheel and spurt straight ahead, onto the truss, over the narrow path suspended high above the water.

Something is terribly wrong here, flashed through Kostya's mind. He should have braked short of the bridge but for some uncanny reason he hadn't done so. His bike carried him onto the truss, onto those same planks, high above the water. . . .

There was no more time to stop, turn or look back. The only way was straight ahead—with no let-up of speed. His hand must not jerk. He knew he couldn't stand the suspense; he'd weaken from fear. But he must go on . . . because of her . . . because her bike was straight ahead. . . .

Kostya couldn't tear his eyes away from the girl. She rode evenly, unswervingly, yet he sensed a desperate tension in that straightness. How can she stand it! Oh, if she only doesn't get it into her head to look back! How far is it to the end of the bridge? If she can only keep her hand from jerking! If only she'll not try to look back! She's over more than half—one more minute, and it'll be all over. Just that she doesn't look back!

The girl did look back.

She turned her head just slightly, just to make sure from the corner of her eye that he was behind. As she turned, her front wheel gave a

slight jerk. A second, a long eternity, she struggled with it, trying to make it straight. But she couldn't. Her bike veered into the air, into emptiness.

He didn't see her fall. She simply disappeared from the bridge—she and her bike. Abruptly he did something he had thought was impossible—he put on the brakes and jumped off onto the planks. He looked down. The water was way, way down, glistening with a dull, firm shine like a metal streaming away, somewhere beyond the bridge. He saw her bike, caught by its frame at the end of a beam, sticking out from behind the rough scaffolding, still swinging slightly. But the girl was nowhere in sight.

Stunned, Kostya put down his bike and dived.

He pierced the surface of the water with his hands and felt it close above him as he was dragged down by the current. Although stung by the fall, he had the presence of mind to open his eyes and look for her. All he could see were hazy outlines of some huge blocks and posts. After touching the bottom, he felt himself pulled up. He turned over under the water and surfaced.

The current pulled him to the bridge span. He came close to a concrete abutment not cleared yet of some wooden casing and piles of lumber. Above, fragments of the cloudy sky seemed to be peeking through the many-storied net of girders, crossbeams and timbering. The current was strong, too strong for any resistance. Kostya drifted with it, turning, whirling, not even trying to fight it until . . . he saw her, just around the bend.

The top of her head appeared behind a pile of timber sticking out of the water at the bridge span. Up to her mouth in water, the girl clutched the pile with both hands, right in front of a foaming whirl. Kostya couldn't see her whole face but her cheek and one eye, and from the look of that eye—large, frightened—he knew that she was holding with her last strength. One more moment and the current would carry her away.

"Hold on!" he shouted, choking on a mouthful of water. Now there was only one thing to be afraid of, that the current would carry him by her. He'd never be able to get back to her against it. Kostya tried desperately to gain control of his movements. His wet breeches and canvas slippers hampered his effort. Nonetheless, he managed to throw out his left arm and grab that same pile. As the current whirled him around and around he hung on, his shoulder touching hers.

The girl's pale, wet face was close to his, her wide-open eyes bright with tension. He hoped she would believe that he would be able to save her. But how? He didn't have the slightest idea himself what to do next.

High up, the concrete abutment towered like a tremendous giant. Its surface was too smooth to offer a hold. Kostya looked back—behind them the river grew wide.

"You know how to swim?" he asked.

She shook her head.

Kostya knew that the girl couldn't hold on much longer. He looked back again; the left bank was not too far away. By himself he'd probably make it. To the right, in the direction of the current, the river made a bend. To the left, oblong stones jutted out of the water. There, he should try to get over there. . . .

He looked at the girl again. He'd have to act fast, as long as she still had some strength left. "Let go," he ordered.

"No, no."

"You must listen to me," he said gravely. He pulled her hand away from the pile and tried to put it on his shoulder. Immediately her other hand slipped off the pile and now the girl clung to him with both hands. Under the burden Kostya let go, and both of them began to sink. The whirl pulled them under. In desperation he forcibly pried open her hands and pushed her away. Thrashing wildly, the girl rose to the surface by herself. He, too, came up, snorted and looked around. The girl kept thrashing right beside him. Her round face rose for a moment out of the water; her mouth gasped for air before she began to sink again. The bridge with all its mass of iron and wood seemed to be rapidly backing away.

Kostya wound her short, chubby arm around his neck. Her other arm which was about to clutch him he pushed aside. "Don't you dare," he said sternly. "You must obey me."

She obeyed and stopped clinging to him. As they began to float more steadily, Kostya struggled stubbornly, stroking with one arm and cutting across the current toward the stones. The girl's soft arm rested confidently though heavily against his neck, pressing his face into the water. But Kostya knew how to handle himself. As long as her face remained above water, he'd be able to lift his head for a breath of air, then let it be submerged.

The girl stopped struggling. She calmed down and obviously had more confidence in him than he had in himself. "I'll do whatever you say," she whispered into his ear. But he felt he was weakening and he was afraid the current would not let them reach the stones. He tried to drift to the shore but the whirls carried him to the right, around the stones, toward the rapids. Two times he tried to reach bottom with his feet; on the third try he touched it.

Although the water reached above his ears, he managed to keep afloat. The shallow from which the stones protruded had apparently extended quite far. Seeing him stand, the girl tried to stand up too. After she swallowed some water and choked, Kostya picked her up and, stepping carefully, he carried her to the shore.

Fifteen minutes later they were sitting on the sloping bank amid elm trees, watching the water through the branches. Their clothes were hung on the trees to dry—he had only his trunks on, she had on panties and a white undershirt. Her semi-nakedness embarrassed him; he tried not to sit too close to her, nor glance at her too often. She, however, seemed not to mind. Her innocent, bright eyes were full of confidence as they admired him through strands of wet hair that kept falling onto her face.

Their bicycles lay side by side on the grass. Kostya had removed them from the bridge by himself. The zeal of achievement had made him feel light and fearless. It hadn't been too difficult to get his bicycle, although when he had stepped onto those planks once again he had asked himself how he was able to ride on that narrow, unfenced path. An hour ago he'd probably not have had the courage to walk on it; but now he ambled without fear, without having to look at his feet. To recover the girl's bike wasn't that easy; he had to clamber down the timbering and hoist the thing with his feet while hanging on the girder with his hands. He had enjoyed his work, however, knowing that she stood there on the shore, watching him, admiring him. He hadn't been afraid to fall into the water because that would have only been a repeat jump. But he had been concerned he might drop the bicycle. He hadn't. He rolled them both up onto the shore, toward the elm tree where their clothes were hung to dry.

"You can do everything," the girl looked at Kostya with admiring eyes.

"I can," he confirmed. "Had I dropped your bike I'd have given you mine." He felt like being extremely generous; as a matter of fact he was sorry he couldn't give her his bike.

"I'd not have taken it for anything," she said. "You are leaving?"

"Yes, tonight."

"For long?"

"Forever."

"And when will you come back?" she asked.

"Probably never."

The impression his words made on her affected him too.

"Never," the girl repeated slowly. "How far are you going?"

"Very far," he replied. "I'm taking the Moscow train tonight."

She asked if he was going to the district capital. She had apparently thought the district capital was very far.

"Uh uh," Kostya said. "The day after tomorrow I'll be in Moscow."

"In Moscow?" she asked respectfully.

"But only for a day," he explained. "Got to do some sightseeing."

"You're going even farther?" she asked incredulously.

He nodded. "To Siberia."

She became quiet. He sensed how impressive that name sounded to her.

"Who's going with you?" she asked again.

"I'm going by myself."

While he answered her questions, Kostya began to see his trip in a new light. He had suddenly made a discovery—he found out something about himself he had never known: he could accomplish tasks. The future, which up to now had appeared fearful, suddenly became a grandiose adventure within reach.

"I'll guide big ships," Kostya said, getting up from excitement. "Diesel motor ships."

"Where to?"

"To the Arctic Ocean. Beyond the Arctic Circle and back. Through the taiga, tundra, all kinds of animals," Kostya recalled what he knew about Siberia. He was waiting for her to ask if he really knew how to guide Diesel motor ships, but she didn't. Perhaps she had some doubts if he really could do everything. He, too, had some doubts.

"I'll learn," he said, thinking of Uncle Vasya. "What one man can do, another man can too."

There was silence for a while. Narrow-shouldered, long-legged, upright, Kostya stared into the water glistening through the trees. Absorbed in his new ideas, he seemed to have forgotten about the girl who sat with her arms around her round knees, glancing at him timidly from time to time.

"Is somebody coming to see you off?" she asked softly.

"They are," he nodded.

"Who?"

Kostya knew that Gramma and Aunt Nadya would come with him to the station, but somehow he didn't feel like telling it to the girl. He made no reply.

"I'll come too. May I?" she asked in a pattering whisper, brushing off her wet hair from her forehead. "We live next to the station; I'll just jump out of the window and run up. May I?" The girl talked fast, as if she were afraid he might stop her. "I won't be in anybody's way; they won't even see me. I'll just watch. May I? May I?"

Kostya didn't answer. He looked at her with a joyous wonderment in his heart—it was a hitherto unknown tenderness which he realized was also a new discovery.

Translated by Selig O. Wassner

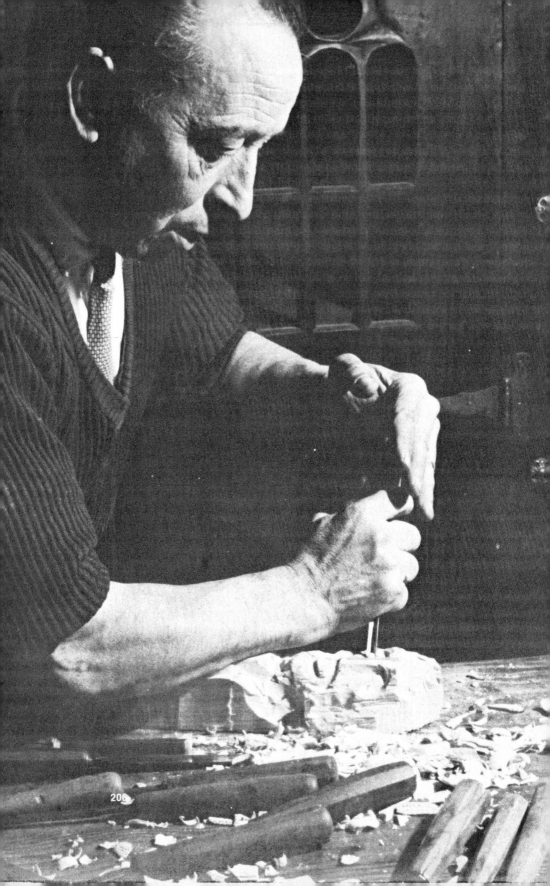

THE BENCH

RICHARD RIVE

EUROPEANS ONLY

"We form an integral part of a complex society, a society in which a vast proportion of the population is denied the very basic right of existence, a society that condemns a man to an inferior position because he has the misfortune to be born black, a society that can only retain its precarious social and economic position at the expense of an enormous oppressed mass!"

The speaker paused for a moment and sipped some water from a glass. Karlie's eyes shone as he listened. Those were great words, he thought, great words and true. Karlie sweated. The hot November sun beat down on the gathering. The trees on the Grand Parade in Johannesburg afforded very little shelter, and his handkerchief was already soaked where he had placed it between his neck and his shirt collar. Karlie stared around him at the sea of faces. Every shade of color was represented, from shiny ebony to the one or two whites in the crowd. Karlie stared at the two detectives who were busily making shorthand notes of the speeches, then turned to stare back at the speaker.

"It is up to us to challenge the right of any group who willfully and deliberately condemn a fellow group to a servile position. We must challenge the right of any people who see fit to segregate human beings solely on grounds of pigmentation. Your children are denied the rights which are theirs by birth. They are segregated educationally, socially, economically. . . ."

Ah, thought Karlie, that man knows what he is speaking about. He says I am as good as any other man, even a white man. That needs much thinking. I wonder if he means I have the right to go to any bioscope, or eat in any restaurant, or that my children can go to a white school. These are dangerous ideas and need much thinking. I wonder what Ou Klaas would say to this. Ou Klaas said that God made the white man and the black man separately, and the one must always be "baas" and the other "jong." But this man says different things and somehow they ring true.

Karlie's brow was knitted as he thought. On the platform were many speakers, both white and black, and they were behaving as if there were no differences of color among them. There was a white woman in a blue dress offering Nxeli a cigarette. That never could have happened at Bietjiesvlei. Old Lategan at the store there would have fainted if his Annatjie had offered Witbooi a cigarette. And Annatjie wore no such pretty dress.

These were new things and he, Karlie, had to be careful before he accepted them. But why shouldn't he accept them? He was not a Colored man any more; he was a human being. The last speaker had said so. He remembered seeing pictures in the newspapers of people who defied laws which relegated them to a particular class, and those people were smiling as they went to prison. This was a queer world.

The speaker continued and Karlie listened intently. He spoke slowly, and his speech was obviously carefully prepared. This is a great man, thought Karlie.

The last speaker was the white lady in the blue dress, who asked them to challenge any discriminatory laws or measures in their own way. Why should she speak like that? She could go to the best bioscopes and swim at the best beaches. Why, she was even more beautiful than Annatjie Lategan.

They had warned him in Bietjiesvlei about coming to the city. He had seen the skollies in District Six and he knew what to expect there. Hanover Street held no terrors for him. But no one had told him about this. This was new; this set one's mind thinking; yet he felt it was true. She had said one should challenge. He, Karlie, would astound old Lategan and Van Wyk at the dairy farm. They could do what they liked to him after that. He would smile like those people in the newspapers.

The meeting was almost over when Karlie threaded his way through the crowd. The words of the speakers were still milling through his head. It could never happen in Bietjiesvlei. Or could it? The sudden screech of a car pulling to a stop whirled him back to his senses. A white head was thrust angrily through the window.

"Look where you're going, you black idiot!"

Karlie stared dazedly at him. Surely this white man never heard what the speakers had said. He could never have seen the white woman offering Nxeli a cigarette. He could never imagine the white lady shouting those words at him. It would be best to catch a train and think these things over.

He saw the station in a new light. Here was a mass of human beings, black, white and some brown like himself. Here they mixed with one another, yet each mistrusted the other with an unnatural fear, each treated the other with suspicion, moved in a narrow, haunted pattern of its own. One must challenge these things the speaker had said . . . in one's own way. Yet how in one's own way? How was one to challenge? Suddenly it dawned upon him. Here was his challenge! *The bench.* The railway bench with "Europeans Only" neatly painted on it in white. For one moment it symbolized all the misery of the plural South African society.

Here was a challenge to his rights as a man. Here it stood. A perfectly ordinary wooden railway bench, like thousands of others in South Africa. His challenge. That bench now had concentrated in it all the evils of a system he could not understand and he felt a victim of. It was the obstacle between himself and humanity. If he sat on it, he was a man. If he was afraid, he denied himself membership as a human being in a human society. He almost had visions of righting this pernicious system, if he only sat down on that bench. Here was his chance. He, Karlie, would challenge.

He seemed perfectly calm when he sat down on the bench, but inside his heart was thumping wildly. Two conflicting ideas now throbbed through him. The one said, "I have no right to sit on this bench." The other was the voice of a new religion and said, "Why have I no right to sit on this bench?" The one voice spoke of the past, of the servile position he had occupied on the farm, of his father, and his father's father who were born black, lived like blacks, and died like mules. The other voice spoke of new horizons and said, "Karlie, you are a man. You have dared what your father and your father's father would not have dared. You will die like a man."

Karlie took out a cigarette and smoked. Nobody seemed to notice his sitting there. This was an anticlimax. The world still pursued its monotonous way. No voice had shouted, "Karlie has conquered!" He was a normal human being sitting on a bench in a busy station, smoking a cigarette. Or was this his victory: the fact that he was a normal human being?

A well-dressed white woman walked down the platform. Would she sit on the bench? Karlie wondered. And then that gnawing voice, "You should stand and let the white woman sit!" Karlie narrowed his eyes and gripped tighter at his cigarette. She swept past him without the slightest twitch of an eyelid and continued walking down the platform. Was she afraid to challenge—to challenge his right to be a human being?

Karlie now felt tired. A third conflicting idea was now creeping in, a compensatory idea which said, "You sit on this bench because you are tired; you are tired therefore you sit." He would not move because he was tired, or was it because he wanted to sit where he liked?

People were now pouring out of a train that had pulled into the station. There were so many people pushing and jostling one another that nobody noticed him. This was his train. It would be easy to step into the train and ride off home, but that would be giving in, suffering defeat, refusing the challenge, in fact, admitting that he was not a human being. He sat on. Lazily he blew the cigarette smoke into the air, thinking. . . . His mind was away from the meeting and the bench: he was thinking of Bietjiesvlei and Ou Klaas, how he had insisted that Karlie should come to Cape Town. Ou Klaas would suck on his pipe and look so quizzically at one. He was wise and knew much. He had said one must go to Cape Town and learn the ways of the world. He would spit and wink slyly when he spoke of District Six and the women he knew in Hanover Street. Ou Klaas knew everything. He said God made us white or black and we must therefore keep our places.

"Get off this seat!"

Karlie did not hear the gruff voice. Ou Klaas would be on the land now waiting for his tot of cheap wine.

"I said get off the bench, you swine!" Karlie suddenly whipped back to reality. For a moment he was going to jump up; then he remembered who he was and why he was sitting there. He suddenly felt very tired. He looked up slowly into a very red face that stared down at him.

"Get up!" it said. "There are benches down there for you."

Karlie looked up and said nothing. He stared into a pair of sharp, gray, cold eyes.

"Can't you hear me speaking to you? You black swine!"

Slowly and deliberately Karlie puffed at the cigarette. This was his test. They both stared at each other, challenged with the eyes, like two boxers, each knowing that they must eventually trade blows yet each afraid to strike first.

"Must I dirty my hands on scum like you?"

Karlie said nothing. To speak would be to break the spell, the supremacy he felt was slowly gaining.

An uneasy silence, then, "I will call a policeman rather than soil my hands on a Hotnot like you. You can't even open up your black jaw when a white man speaks to you."

Karlie saw the weakness. The white man was afraid to take action himself. He, Karlie, had won the first round of the bench dispute.

A crowd had now collected.

"*Afrika!*" shouted a joker.

Karlie ignored the remark. People were now milling around him, staring at the unusual sight of a black man sitting on a white man's bench. Karlie merely puffed on.

"Look at him. That's the worst of giving these Kaffirs enough rope."

"I can't understand it. They have their own benches!"

"Don't get up! You have every right to sit there!"

"He'll get up when a policeman comes!"

"After all, why shouldn't they sit there?"

"I've said before: I've had a native servant once, and a more impertinent . . ."

Karlie sat and heard nothing. Irresolution had now turned to determination. Under no condition was he going to get up. They could do what they liked.

"So, this is the fellow, eh! Get up there! Can't you read?"

The policeman was towering over him. Karlie could see the crest on his buttons and the wrinkles in his neck.

"What is your name and address? Come on!"

Karlie still maintained his obstinate silence. It took the policeman rather unawares. The crowd was growing every minute.

"You have no right to speak to this man in such a manner!" It was the white lady in the blue dress.

"Mind your own business! I'll ask your help when I need it. It's people like you who make these Kaffirs think they're as good as white men. Get up, you!" The latter remark was addressed to Karlie.

"I insist that you treat him with proper respect."

The policeman turned red.

"This . . . this . . ." He was lost for words.

"Kick up the Hotnot if he won't get up!" shouted a spectator. Rudely a white man laid hands on Karlie.

"Get up, you!" Karlie turned to resist, to cling to the bench, his bench. There was more than one man pulling at him. He hit out wildly and then felt a dull pain as somebody rammed a fist into his face. He was bleeding now and wild-eyed. He would fight for it. The constable clapped a pair of handcuffs on him and tried to clear a way through the crowd. Karlie still struggled. A blow or two landed on him. Suddenly he relaxed and slowly struggled to his feet. It was useless to fight any longer. Now it was his turn to smile. He had challenged and won. Who cared the rest? "Come on, you swine!" said the policeman forcing Karlie through the crowd.

"Certainly!" said Karlie for the first time. And he stared at the policeman with all the arrogance of one who dared sit on a "European bench."

JANAKI

SANTHA RAMA RAU

It was at Joe's Place that Anand announced the arrival of Janaki. I had got there early, I remember, and was sitting at our table when Anand came in. He always had a certain tension in his walk, but that day it seemed more pronounced. He held his narrow shoulders stiffly and carried an air of trouble, so I asked him at once whether anything was the matter.

"Matter?" he asked sharply, as though it were an archaic word. "Why should anything be the matter?"

"Well, I don't know. You just look funny."

"Well, I don't feel funny," he said, deliberately misunderstanding. Then he looked at me in silence, with a portentous frown. At last he said, "Do you *know* what they've gone and done *now?* They've invited a cousin—a *distant* cousin—to stay."

This didn't seem to me any great disaster. Cousins, invited or not, were eternally coming to visit. Any relatives had the right to turn up whenever it was convenient for them and stay as long as they liked. His announcement came as an anticlimax; but since he did seem so distressed, I asked carefully, "And I suppose you'll be expected to fit him into the firm in some capacity?"

"Her," Anand said. "It's a girl."

"A *girl?* Is *she* going to work in the business?"

"Oh, of *course* not. Can't you see what they're up to?"

"Well, no, I can't."

"Don't you *see?*" he said, looking helpless before such stupidity. "They're trying to arrange a marriage for me."

I could think of nothing to say except an unconvincing, "Surely not."

He went on without paying any attention. "I dare say they think they're being subtle. Throwing us together, you know, so that my incomprehensible, *foreign*—" he emphasized the word bitterly—"preference for making up my own mind about these things will not be offended. We are to grow imperceptibly fond of each other. Oh, I see the whole plot."

"You must be imagining it all."

"She arrived last night. They didn't even tell me she was coming."

"Poor Anand." I was sorry for him, and angry on his behalf. There had never been any romantic exchanges between Anand and me, so the girl didn't represent any personal threat; but I honestly thought that a matter of principle was involved and that one should stand by the principle. We had so often agreed that the system of arranged marriages was the ultimate insult to one's rights as a human being, the final, insupportable interference of domineering families. I tried to think of something comforting to say, but could only produce feebly, "Well, all you have to do is sit it out."

"And watch her doing little chores around the house? Making herself quietly indispensable?" He added with a sour smile, "As the years roll by. Do you suppose we will grow old gracefully together?"

"Oh, don't be such a fool," I said, laughing. "She'll have to go, sooner or later."

"But will I live that long?" He seemed to be cheering up.

"It's rather unfair to the poor thing," I said, thinking for the first time of the girl. "I mean, if they've got her hopes up."

"Now, don't start sympathizing with *her*. The only way to finish the thing once and for all to make my position clear is to marry someone else immediately. I suppose you wouldn't consider marrying me, would you?"

"Heavens, no," I said, startled. "I don't think you need to be as drastic as that."

"Well, perhaps not. We'll see."

At last I thought to ask, "What's she called?"

"Janaki."

"Pretty name."

"It makes me vomit."

I could hardly wait for our next lunch date, and when we met a couple of days later at Joe's Place I started questioning Anand eagerly. "Well, how are things? How are you making out with Janaki?"

"Janaki? Oh, she's all right, I suppose. A minor pest."

"Is she being *terribly* sweet to you?"

"Oh, you know. I will say this for her, she manages to be pretty unobtrusive."

"Oh." I was obscurely disappointed.

"It's just knowing she's always *there* that's so infuriating."

"It would drive me crazy."

In a voice that was suddenly cross, he said, "She's so *womanly*."

"Hovers about, you mean?"

"Not that, so much, but I can see her *hoping* I'll eat a good dinner or have had a good day at the office, or some damn thing."

"It sounds rather flattering."

"I dare say that's the strategy. It's pathetic, really, how little they know me if they think she's the sort of girl I'd want to marry."

"What sort of girl *would* you want to marry?"

"Heaven knows," Anand said in a hopeless voice. "Someone quite different, anyway. . . ."

As we left Joe's Place after lunch, he said, "I think you'd better come to tea to meet her. Would you like to?"

"I was hoping you'd ask me."

"OK, then. Tomorrow?"

Full of excitement the next day, I met Anand after work and drove home with him. "Is your mother going to be cross about your asking me?"

"Why should she be cross? You've been to tea with us before."

"But that was different."

"I can't see why," he said, refusing to accept the situation.

"Oh, don't be so dense," I said, thinking, poor girl, it's going to be very frustrating for her if he insists on treating her as a casual cousin come for a holiday. "Does your mother tactfully leave you alone with her for tea?"

"Never. The two of them chatter about domestic details. It's really very boring."

To me it was far from boring. For one thing, Anand's mother was far more cordial to me than she had been on previous visits, and I wondered whether she could already be so sure of the success of her plan that I was no longer a danger. And then there was the suspense of waiting to see what Janaki would be like.

She came in with the servant who carried the tea tray, holding back the curtain of the dining-room archway so that he could manage more easily. A plump, graceful girl with a very pretty face and a tentative, vulnerable smile, which she seemed ready to cancel at once if you weren't going to smile with her. I saw, instantly, that she was any mother-in-law's ideal—quiet, obedient, helpful. Her hair was drawn back into the conventional knot at the nape of her neck; she wore no make-up except for the faintest touch of lipstick, and even that, I decided, was probably a new experiment for her, a concession to Anand's Westernized tastes.

She spoke mostly to Anand's mother, in Gujerati, and I noticed that she had already assumed some of the duties of a hostess. She poured the tea, asked, in clear, lilting English, whether I took milk and sugar, and handed around the plates of Indian savories and sweets.

After the first mouthful, I remarked formally, "This is delicious."

Anand's mother caught the tone, even if she didn't understand the words, and said something in Gujerati to Anand.

He translated, without much interest. "Janaki made them."

I quickly said the first thing that came into my head, "How clever you are. I wish I could cook."

"It is very easy to learn," she replied.

"There never seems to be any time for it."

Entirely without sarcasm or envy she said, "That is true for someone like you who leads such a busy and interesting life."

I felt ashamed of myself, for no reason I could quite put my finger on.

Janaki saw me to the front door and, with an unexpected spontaneity, put her hand on my arm. "Please come to tea again," she said. "I mean, if you are not too occupied. I should so much like it. I have no friends in Bombay."

"I'd be delighted, and you must come to tea with me."

"Oh, no, thank you very much. Perhaps later on, but I must learn the ways of this house first. You see that, don't you?"

I walked home, wondering at her mixture of nervousness and confidence, at the fact that she already felt certain she had a permanent place in that house.

At our next lunch date, it was Anand who asked the eager questions. "Well? What did you think of her?"

And I replied noncommittally, "She seemed very pleasant."

"Quite the little housewife, do you mean?"

"No. Sweet and anxious to please, I meant."

"You sound like my mother. She says, 'A good-natured girl. You should count yourself fortunate.' I suppose she asked you to be her friend?"

"How did you know?"

"She's not as stupid as she looks. She said the same to me. 'Will you not allow us to be friendly, Anand?'" He attempted a saccharin, unconvincing falsetto. He frowned. "It would be funny if it weren't so sad."

"Well, at least she's very good-looking," I said defensively.

"She's too fat."

"I think it rather suits her."

"A strong point in her favor, my mother says, to make up for my puniness." Anand was sensitive about his height. He said, in a touchy voice, daring one to sympathize with him, "Eugenically very sound. Strong, healthy girl like Janaki married to a weakling like me, and we have a chance of strong, healthy children that take after her. The children, you see, are the whole point of this stratagem. I'm an only son and must produce some. My mother has a rather simple approach to these things."

"You must admit," I said rather uncomfortably, "that she'd make a very good mother."

"Not a doubt in the world. She's a natural for the part of the Great Earth Mother. But I rather resent being viewed in such an agricultural light."

In the weeks that followed, Janaki dominated our conversation at lunchtime, and I had tea with them quite frequently. Sometimes, if Anand was kept late at his office or had to attend a board meeting, Janaki and I would have tea alone, and she would ask hundreds of questions about America, trying, I thought, to build up a picture of Anand's life there and the background that seemed to influence him so much.

She would question me, sometimes openly and sometimes indirectly, about Anand's tastes and preferences. We had a long session, I remember, about her looks. Should she wear make-up? Should she cut her hair? What about her clothes? I told her she was fine the way she was, but she insisted, "Has he *never* said anything? He must have made *some* remark?"

"Well," I said reluctantly, "he did once mention that he thought you were just a fraction on the chubby side."

Without a trace of rancor, Janaki said, "I will quickly become thin."

"Heavens! Don't take the remark so seriously."

"It is nothing," Janaki assured me. "One need only avoid rice and *ghi*." She did, too. I noticed the difference in a couple of weeks.

When Anand was there, the atmosphere was much more strained. From the frigid politeness of his early days with Janaki, his manner gradually changed to irritation, which expressed itself in angry silence and later in a kind of undercover teasing sometimes laced with malice. For instance, he would greet her with something like, "What have you been up to today? Hemstitching the sheets? Crocheting for the hope chest?" and Janaki would look puzzled and smile, as though she had missed the point of a clever joke.

One couldn't help disliking him in this role of tormentor. The fact was, of course, that, in Anand's phrase, *I* was getting imperceptibly fonder of Janaki as his impatience with her grew more overt. There was, to me, both gallantry and an appealing innocence in her undaunted conviction that everything would turn out all right. What I didn't recognize was the solid realism behind her attitude. I started to suspect the calculation in her nature one day when Anand had been particularly difficult. He had insisted on talking about books she hadn't read and, with apparent courtesy, addressing remarks to her he knew she couldn't answer.

Janaki said nothing for a long time and then admitted, with a becoming lack of pretension, "I'm afraid I read only the stories in the *Illustrated Weekly*. But, Anand, if you would bring me some books you think good, I would read them."

"I'll see if I can find the time," he replied in a surly voice.

When Janaki showed me to the door that evening, I said in considerable exasperation, "Why do you put up with it? He needn't be so disagreeable when he talks to you."

"It is natural that there should be difficulties at first. After his life in America, there are bound to be resentments here."

"Well, I think you are altogether too forbearing. I wouldn't stand it for a second." Privately, I had begun to think she must, after all, be stupid.

Then Janaki said, "What would you do?"

"Leave, of course. Go back." And at that moment I realized what she meant. Go back to what? To another betrothal arranged by her elders? Learning to please some other man? Here, at least, she liked her future mother-in-law.

"And besides," she said, "I know that really he is kind."

In the end, Janaki turned out to be the wisest of us all, and I have often thought how lucky it was that she didn't follow my advice then. Not that Anand capitulated all at once, or that one extraordinary morning he suddenly saw her with new eyes, or anything like that.

I noticed it first one day when he finished his lunch rather hurriedly and said, as we were going back to our offices, "That girl's conversation is driving me nuts. I think I really had better buy her some books. As long as I'm stuck with her company," he added awkwardly.

We parted at the bookshop, and in later conversations I learned that Janaki was doing her homework with diligence and pleasure.

From then on things moved fairly rapidly. I began to anticipate Anand's frequent suggestions that we spend part of the lunch hour shopping—usually rather ungraciously expressed—"We've got to get that girl into some less provincial-looking saris." "That girl listens to nothing but film music. I really must get her some decent classical stuff. What do you suggest as a beginning?"

"No Western music?" I asked pointedly.

"She wouldn't understand it," Anand replied.

All the same, at home he continued to be offhand or overbearing with her. She remained calm and accepting, a willing pupil who knew that her stupidity was a great trial to her teacher. Still, there wasn't a doubt in my mind about the change of attitude going on in Anand.

Anand's parents were evidently equally confident of the outcome, for one day at tea he announced, with an exuberance no amount of careful casualness could disguise, that his father was going to send him to New York on a business trip. He was pleased, he insisted, largely because it meant that at last he was to be trusted with some real responsibility.

I said, "And it will be such wonderful fun to be back in America."

We were absorbed in discussing the details of the trip, and besides, by then Janaki had become such an accepted—and pleasing—part of the scenery of the house that we assumed she was listening with her usual attention and, as always, trying to fit in with Anand's mood.

So it came as quite a shock when she suddenly spoke in a flat, decisive voice. "I, too, am leaving. I am going back to my home." Dead silence for a moment. "Tomorrow," she said.

"But *why*—" I began.

"It is my decision," she said, and wouldn't look at either of us.

Anand didn't say anything, just stood up, with all his bright, important planning gone, and walked out of the room. We waited to hear his study door slam.

Then my affection for Janaki (and, of course, curiosity) made me ask, "But why *now,* just when things are going so well?"

"It was your advice, don't you remember?"

"But things were different then."

"Yes." She nodded as though we both recognized some particular truth.

At the time I thought she believed herself defeated. I was surprised and concerned that what seemed so plain to me should remain obscure to her. "Listen," I said cautiously, "don't you see that he—that in spite of everything, he has fallen in love with you?"

I don't know quite what I had expected her response to be—a radiant smile, perhaps, or even a sense of triumph. I hadn't expected her to glare at me as though I were an enemy and say, "Oh, love. I don't want him to *love* me. I want him to marry me."

"It's different for him," I said, as persuasively as I could. "For him it is important."

She looked at me shrewdly, making up her mind about something. "You are sure?" she asked.

"Absolutely sure."

Her voice was hard and impatient. "Love, what books you read, whether you like music, your 'taste'—whatever that may mean. As if all that has anything to do with marriage."

"Well," I said ineffectually.

How can one make the idea of romantic love attractive to someone who wants only a home, a husband, and children? Even if nothing could be done about that, I thought I knew the reason for her sudden despair. The renewing of Anand's American experiences must have seemed to her an overwhelming menace. I tried to reassure her, reminded her that Anand would be gone only a matter of weeks, that he would miss her, that America would look quite different to him now, that he had changed a lot in the past year—more than a year, actually.

But she wouldn't listen, and she kept repeating, "I must pack my things and leave the house tomorrow."

I thought, Poor Janaki. It didn't occur to me that I might equally have thought, Clever Janaki, the only one of us who knows exactly what she wants. Leave the house? She would have slit her throat first.

When I think of it, I can't help wondering at the extent of my naiveté then. The fact is that women—or perhaps I mean just the women of a certain kind of world, Janaki's world—have inherited, through bitter centuries, a ruthless sense of self-preservation. It still seems to me ghastly that they should need it; but it would be silly to deny that, in most places on earth, they still do. That cool, subtle determination to find her security and hang on to it, that all's-fair attitude—not in love, which she discounted, but in war, for it *was* war, the gaining or losing of a kingdom—was really no more than the world deserved from Janaki. As in war, victory, conquest, success, call it what you will, was the only virtue. And, of course, the really absurd thing was that nobody would have been more appalled than Janaki if you had called her a feminist.

As it was, I heard with anxiety Anand on the phone the next day, saying, "Let's lunch. I want to talk to you. Joe's Place? One o'clock?"

I was certain that Janaki had gone home, with only the indignities of a few new clothes and a lot of tiresome talk to remember.

As soon as I saw him, I knew I was wrong. He had the conventionally sheepish look that makes the announcing of good news quite pointless. He said, "An eventful evening, wasn't it?"

"Yes, it was, rather."

Then there was a long pause while he looked embarrassed and I could think of no way to help him out. At last he said, all in a rush. "Look, this is going to seem ridiculous. I mean—well, Janaki and I are going to be married."

"You couldn't do a more sensible thing," I said, much relieved.

He looked startled. "Sensible? Perhaps it seems that way to you. Actually, we're in love with each other."

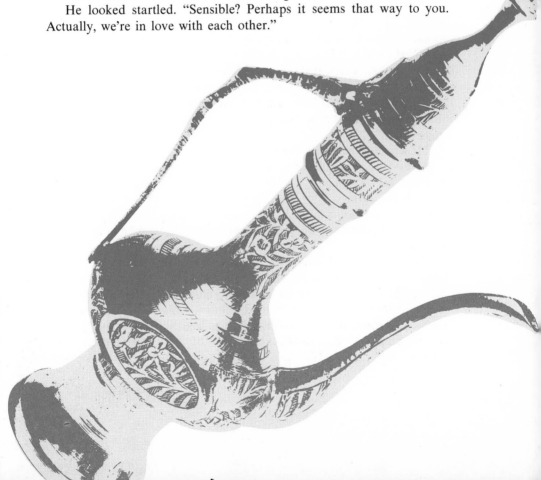

"With *each other?*" I echoed incredulously, and regretted it immediately.

"I knew it would seem peculiar to you. I daresay you've thought I hated her all this time." He smiled at me in a rather superior way. "I thought so myself for a while. And Janaki, as you well imagine, had every reason to think so. And I must say it certainly took a lot of courage on her part. I mean, when you think——"

"You'd better start at the beginning," I said, suddenly feeling depressed.

"OK. I heard you leave yesterday, and then I heard Janaki come into the hall—you know that timid way she has of walking—and stand outside my study door. I was in quite a state; but I daresay that I wouldn't have done anything about anything if she hadn't—I mean, if someone hadn't taken the initiative."

"Yes," I said, knowing what was coming but unable to shake off my gloom. "She came to explain why she was going home."

"She said—you see, she isn't the passive, orthodox girl you think—she told me that quite against her plans or anything she's expected, she'd—I know this will seem silly—but she'd fallen in love with me."

"I see. And that accounted for her behavior. Trying all the time to please you, I mean."

"Well, yes. Then I realized that—"

"All your resentment and bad manners were just that—" I wanted to hurry him through the story.

"Well, yes."

"Well, yes," I repeated, and couldn't look at him. We were silent for a while. "Well, congratulations," I said uneasily.

"It's funny, isn't it," he said in a confident voice, "that their plans should have worked out—but so differently. I don't suppose they'll ever understand."

"It wouldn't be worth trying to explain."

"Heavens, no. Look, I'm taking Janaki out to lunch tomorrow. Will you join us?"

"Oh, no, surely—"

"She asked particularly that you come. She likes you very much, you know, and besides, she doesn't feel quite comfortable going out without a chaperon."

"In *that* case—" I said, with a nastiness lost on Anand. And all the time I was thinking, have we all been made use of? A sympathetic mother-in-law, a man you can flatter, a gullible friend from whom you can learn background and fighting conditions, with whom you can check tactics and their effects. Now that she has won, she must have nothing but contempt for all of us. But simultaneously I was wondering, is she, after all, really in love? It was a state she didn't know how to cope with,

224

and she could hope only to use the weapon she knew, an ability to please or try to please. Why should she, or how could she, tell me all that herself—a realm of which she was so unsure, which was so far out of her experience?

Now that I have met so many Janakis of the world, I think I know which explanation was right.

"So we'll meet," Anand was saying, "at the Taj, if that's all right with you?"

He had reserved a table by the windows. Janaki was a bit late, to be sure—she explained breathlessly—that we would be there before her, because it would have been agony to sit alone.

We ordered from the Indian menu, and Anand said, with only a fleeting, questioning glance at me, "No wine, I think. There really isn't any wine at all that goes with Indian food, is there?"

EVICTED

FLORENCIO SANCHEZ

Characters

LANDLADY
FIRST TENANT
SECOND TENANT
TWO LABORERS
INDALECIA, the evicted tenant
SOLDIER, her father
INDALECIA'S CHILDREN
JENARO, another tenant, an Italian junk peddler
A YOUNGSTER
POLICE COMMISSIONER
REPORTER
PHOTOGRAPHER
HIS ASSISTANT

Place and Time: Tenement yard. Contemporary Buenos Aires, Argentina

LANDLADY (*coming out of the rooms of the first tenant*). You know, don't you? And don't forget. I'm tired of waiting till tomorrow or sometime later.

FIRST TENANT. But what can you do? When you can't, you can't.

LANDLADY. Then don't rent the room. This is a republic, isn't it? And the rent is the thing that matters.

FIRST TENANT. All right, all right! It isn't necessary to talk so much.

LANDLADY. That's what I say. All this talk is unnecessary. You pay by the end of the month and we'll forget all about it. (*Walking away*) Yes, sir. There's no need for so much pride. (*Banging into a table*) Oh! Ouch!

FIRST TENANT (*aside*). I wish you'd broken something.

LANDLADY. Oh, confound it! (*She strikes the table angrily and turns in wrath to* INDALECIA.) Are you going to keep this junk in the patio forever? Aren't you ashamed?

INDALECIA. But, señora, I only——

LANDLADY. The devil! If they'd thrown this trash into the street, you wouldn't have been here so long either. It's unbelievable. Ouch!

SECOND TENANT (*coming closer*). Did you hurt yourself very much, ma'am?

LANDLADY. How do I know? I hit myself awful hard.

FIRST TENANT (*mockingly*). Yes, they might turn into cancers. Better call the hospital.

LANDLADY. Look here, Francisca. Come here. (*She steps behind a piece of furniture to examine her injured leg. A couple of laborers, who are heading for the street, stop and stare.*)

SECOND TENANT. The nerve of them!

LANDLADY. Look, right here on this leg! (*She sees the men.*) What do you want? Is that all you have to do?

SECOND TENANT. *Ave Maria!* Such curiosity! (*The two laborers go away, laughing.*)

FIRST TENANT (*calling after them*). Hey, Juan, do you know whether the Southern Mutual Admiration Society is having a dance Saturday night?

JUAN. I guess so. (*Exit the laborers.*)

FIRST TENANT. I'm not invited. The party is for you members only. Ha! Ha! (*Starts out.*)

SECOND TENANT. Funny, aren't you?

LANDLADY. Let her go. It's not worthwhile to argue.

SECOND TENANT. You're right. Come on to my room. I'll give you a rubdown with alcohol. Come on. It's certainly true. You can hardly move around in this patio.

LANDLADY. I should say not, with all this clutter of furniture.

SECOND TENANT. One day is all right, maybe two, but any longer is too long.

INDALECIA (*sadly*). Oh, señora, pray to God that you never get into any such trouble.

SECOND TENANT. Don't worry. As long as he gives me health to work, I'll get along. I'm not the kind that waits with folded arms for heaven to shower gifts down on me.

LANDLADY. That's what I say. Look, Indalecia, don't think I'm doing this because I want to. I've got a heart, see? But a person can't keep on inconveniencing people all the time. . . .

INDALECIA. What can I do? Do you want me to throw myself into the river with all my children?

SECOND TENANT. We didn't say that, but you can go someplace else. You can look for work. In Buenos Aires there are plenty of ways to earn a living.

INDALECIA. For heaven's sake, that's all I've done—look for a job—and you know it. They wouldn't give out sewing to an old woman like me. I can't go to a factory or hire out as a servant because I have to look after the children.

LANDLADY. Well, tell me something. Was it necessary to have so many children? If you can't look after them, have them and get rid of them.

SECOND TENANT. Yes, what about an orphan asylum?

INDALECIA. It's easy to say that. The poor children!

LANDLADY. Poor children! Poor children! And meantime they run around dying of hunger, stealing food like cats from other people's houses.

(*Enter* JENARO *in time to hear the last words.*)

JENARO (*with a marked Italian accent*). That's what they should do when the other people are so stingy. Let them throw you out of here, Indalecia. They're a bunch of no-goods. The idea of treating a poor woman this way! Such brutes!

SECOND TENANT. Come on, ma'am, let's look at that wound.

LANDLADY (*to* JENARO). Tell me something! What are you hinting? Just tell me!

JENARO (*muttering without paying any attention to her*). Such brutes! (*To* INDALECIA.) Don't worry. Didn't anybody come?

INDALECIA. Nobody.

(JENARO *starts for his room, upstage left.*)

LANDLADY (*stopping here*). Look here. What are you hinting?

JENARO. Are you speaking to me?

LANDLADY (*angrily*). Yes, to you. To you!

(JENARO *stares at her for a moment, then makes a characteristic Neapolitan gesture. He enters his room and slams the door behind him.*)

LANDLADY (*furiously*). Swindler! Ragamuffin!

SECOND TENANT. That junk man is drunk. Don't pay any attention to him!

LANDLADY. The dirty dog!

SECOND TENANT. Come on and let's look after your leg. Forget him!

LANDLADY. Ragamuffin! (*Turning to* INDALECIA) And you, too, for being such a nuisance. Tomorrow I'm going to have all your trash thrown into the street. I'm sick of the bother. (*Goes out muttering, following the* TENANT.)

INDALECIA (*putting down her sewing and going to the cradle*). Wake up, baby! You mustn't spend the whole day sleeping. Are you sick? Do you hurt anywhere? No? Well, then, upsy daisy! (*Lifts her*) Want a piece of bread? (*Takes a crust from her pocket and gives it to the baby*) Tonight they'll bring us money, lots of money, and we'll eat plenty. Plenty! Are you hungry?

(JENARO *reappears with a cheese, a loaf of bread and a big knife in his hands. He approaches* INDALECIA *and cuts off a piece of cheese.*)

JENARO. Here. Take this. Eat it.

INDALECIA. Oh, you needn't have troubled.

JENARO. Eat it, I tell you. (*He takes a bun from his pocket and gives it to the baby.*) Eat something, won't you? Where are the children?

INDALECIA. I don't know. In the street, probably.

JENARO (*going to the door, calls*). Hey, you! Come here, you. And you, too!

(*Three youngsters appear.* JENARO *gives a piece of bread to each one.*)

JENARO. Here, take it. Go on and eat it. (*The boys take the bread eagerly and begin eating.*)

INDALECIA. Ungrateful children! What do you say?

ONE BOY (*with mouth full*). Thank you.

JENARO (*gesturing them toward the door*). Now you can go! (*To* INDALECIA) No, Indalecia. There's no need for politeness. They're hungry. They eat. And that's the end of it.

(*Exit the children.* JENARO *sits down somewhere. He takes a hunk of salami from his pocket and begins eating. Pause.*)

JENARO. I was at the hospital. They operated on your husband.

INDALECIA. What? Again?

JENARO. Yes. That's right. (*Gets up*) Here, try some of this salami.

INDALECIA. They'll kill him. (*Takes the salami and gives it to the baby.*)

JENARO (*sitting down again*). That would be the best thing. He's always going to be paralyzed.

INDALECIA. Poor Daniel! Did you talk to him?

JENARO. They wouldn't let me see him. There wasn't any need to, anyway. (*Pause*) What did the landlady say to you?

INDALECIA. The usual things. Muttered. Insulted me.

JENARO. What brutes!

INDALECIA. They're all so cruel. Look, I forgive her because, after all, she's the landlady. But the others, the rest of the tenants. Heartless, all of them. If they were happier, or better than me, nobody would have anything to say. But they're devils. Maybe they have a right to, but—no. They're poor people like me. They have children like me, and a working husband who risks death every day from some machine or some scaffold. And instead of thinking once in a while that they might find themselves in my position tomorrow or the next day, they're all alike in criticizing me. And all to get into her good graces. Do you think there was one in the whole house who'd offer me a bit of soup for the baby? No, indeed. They'd rather throw their leftovers into the gutter.

JENARO. What brutes!

INDALECIA (*with tears in her voice*). That's the thing that hurts me most, to see that a person is nobody, that suddenly you're alone in the world, all by yourself, abandoned by everybody, worse than a dog. (*Weeps*)

JENARO. No, no! But what good does it do to let it get you down? Shut up and stop crying, won't you!

(Noise and yells are now heard outside. "Crazy old man! Drunken old man!" A group of youngsters appear, including INDALECIA*'s children, plaguing a crippled veteran of the Paraguay War.)*

SOLDIER *(shaking his cane at the children)*. Shame on you! With youngsters like you, how are they going to make a nation?

INDALECIA. Daddy!

JENARO *(to the children)*. Get out of here! Confound it. Shame on you! Go away!

SOLDIER. Thank you, sir. It's unbelievable.

JENARO. That's the way children are.

SOLDIER. But don't you see, man? It shows what the country has come to. Foreigners like you have to protect the defenders of this country. Look here, friend. I'm Corporal Morante, and you can ask anyone who was in the war whether I won this decoration, or this other one, for nothing.

JENARO. All right, but what are we going to do?

SOLDIER. What do you mean, what are we going to do? Make them respectful, for heaven's sake! *(To* INDALECIA*)* How are you getting along, daughter?

INDALECIA. Oh, so so. But what are you doing around here?

SOLDIER. I came to see you. And this is the way you receive me. Why, even the children are ungrateful.

INDALECIA. How did you find where I was?

SOLDIER. I heard about your troubles. I was in the saloon of old one-eyed Ramos, in Palermo, and someone was reading in a newspaper about how you were driven out of your home and how they were starting to collect contributions to help you. "Confound it," says I, "that's my daughter. Poor girl, where does she live?" On such and such a street, the man with the paper told me. "I must see what kind of trouble Indalecia's in," I says, and here I am, and if I can help you in any way, even though I'm a cripple, don't forget that you're my daughter.

INDALECIA. You might have remembered that long ago.

SOLDIER. You made your choice. You were determined to run off with that good-for-nothing husband.

INDALECIA. Let's not talk about him.

SOLDIER. All right, we won't, if you don't want to, but I told you you'd be unhappy with him and look how it turned out. He fell from a scaffold, didn't he?

INDALECIA. Yes.

SOLDIER. Don't you see? Just what I said. Is this baby yours? Come here, baby. Come to your grandfather. *(The child, frightened, toddles to its*

232

mother.) You see! This country is in a terrible state, foreigner. The grandchildren won't go to their grandfathers. There's no respect for family or anything. In our time you should have seen the respect. And the rest of these kids, are they yours, too? So you were the ones who were insulting your old grandfather. I'll show you, youngsters! (*Starts toward the boys*.)

INDALECIA. Daddy!

JENARO (*stopping him*). Hey! Stop bothering!

SOLDIER. Who gave you the right to interfere? What about him, Indalecia? Is he another son-in-law? At least you might pay her rent, pal.

INDALECIA. Leave him alone, Daddy. If you've come to insult people you should have stayed away.

SOLDIER. All right. But I'm going to sit down now, even if you don't invite me to. (*Sits down. Pause*) Have they brought you the money they collected for you?

INDALECIA. No, not yet.

SOLDIER. You know, I can't help you very much because I'm broke, and I live in the barracks of my old regiment, but if you like, I can look for a place for you to move to. I saw one today on Soler Street.

INDALECIA. Don't bother!

SOLDIER. What do you intend to do?

INDALECIA. I don't know. Nothing!

SOLDIER. Wait a minute! There's an orphan asylum for soldiers' children. There—Say, if I wasn't in bad with the Colonel, I could ask him to use his influence. (*Enter the* LANDLADY.)

INDALECIA. What for?

SOLDIER. So you could put the whole caboodle of kids in the asylum. What are you going to do with them?

LANDLADY. That's what I told her. Put them into an asylum. They aren't worth anything except to make more work.

SOLDIER. How do you do, ma'am?

INDALECIA. No, sir, I won't be separated from my children. If the rest of you have no heart, I have, and in its right place too.

LANDLADY. But tell me something. Isn't it worse for them to die of hunger, with nothing to eat?

SOLDIER. You're right. Shake hands. (*To* INDALECIA) Who is this lady?

LANDLADY. I'm the landlady.

SOLDIER (*with change of attitude*). Oho! You're the one who's kicking them head over heels into the street!

LANDLADY. Well, naturally, if they don't pay their rent.

SOLDIER. And you have the nerve to offer advice! You just get out of here!

LANDLADY. And who do you think you are? I'm the owner of this house, I'd like you to know.

SOLDIER. And a fine owner you are, you miserable——

233

LANDLADY. That's enough of that. (*To* INDALECIA) And does this character think this is a parlor for visitors? Will you be kind enough to get rid of this old drunk.

SOLDIER. The devil take your whole family, you damned foreigner! (*Enter* JENARO.)

JENARO. In God's mercy, will you let this poor woman alone. (*Takes the arm of the* LANDLADY *to pull her away*) Go somewhere else, will you, before I push your face in.

LANDLADY (*angrily*). Get out, you pig. You dirty dog.

JENARO (*shoving her violently*). Get out! (*To the* SOLDIER) And you, too. What brutes!

SOLDIER. Don't you dare touch me! Don't you come near me, you foreigner. (*Struggle. Yells. Neighbors come in. The* LANDLADY *talks loudly.*)

INDALECIA. Calm yourself, don Jenaro.

JENARO (*slapping the* LANDLADY *across the face*). What brutes!

SOLDIER. One side, Indalecia. I can still handle this foreigner.

(*Enter the* COMMISSIONER OF POLICE *and a* REPORTER, *with a crowd of youngsters.*)

COMMISSIONER. What's going on here? Come, come! Calm down! I'm the Police Commissioner of this district of the city.

LANDLADY. Look here, Commissioner. This scoundrel of a junk man hit me a terrible blow.

SOLDIER (*saluting*). At your service, sir.

JENARO (*starting toward his room*). What brutes!

LANDLADY. Don't let him escape, Commissioner. He struck me. And he's a good for nothing.

COMMISSIONER (*to* JENARO). Hey, there. Wait a minute. What's happened?

LANDLADY. Look, Commissioner. Arrest him!

COMMISSIONER. Silence!

SOLDIER. I'm a witness, sir. Nothing has happened. Just a lot of talk, that's all, I swear it. (*Raises his hand.*)

COMMISSIONER. Put your hand down. Now, then. All of you, clear out!

LANDLADY. But Mr. Police Commissioner.

COMMISSIONER. Clear out, I said.

(LANDLADY *starts away muttering. Before she disappears, she looks with hate at* JENARO *and kisses her crossed finger at him, in a threatening gesture.*)

COMMISSIONER (*to* INDALECIA, *who is surrounded by her children*). Now, then, who's the owner of this furniture?

SOLDIER (*points at* INDALECIA). It's hers, sir. She's my daughter.

COMMISSIONER. Very well. I'm the Police Commissioner from this district and this gentleman is a reporter. We heard that you're in trouble and——

REPORTER. My paper was the first to carry the story.

SOLDIER. I can vouch for that. Didn't I tell you, daughter, that I had heard someone read it?

REPORTER. Then you probably know that we started making a fund for her. I'm here to bring her all that we have received so far. Maybe it isn't much, but it's enough to let her rent a room and get herself the necessities of life.

SOLDIER. Thank him, daughter.

REPORTER. Here are sixty pesos, and the list of the people who sent money to my paper. Here!

(INDALECIA *starts crying as she clutches the youngsters. All show emotion.* JENARO *wipes his eyes on his sleeve.*)

REPORTER. Don't take it so hard, ma'am. You'll see. Things can be remedied. Calm yourself. Take your money.

SOLDIER. That's a fine way. When they bring you salvation, you start crying. You should have done that before. (*Takes the money and pushes it toward her*) Here, take it and say thank you.

CHILD. Mama! Mama!

INDALECIA (*soothingly*). That's all right. Many thanks. Don't cry, baby. Don't cry. See, Mama isn't crying. Come on. Dry your eyes. (*She wipes her face and blows her nose in her apron.*) Now be a good little girl. These are nice men. Thank you, gentlemen. Thank you.

REPORTER. The Commissioner has also done something for her. He'll tell you.

COMMISSIONER. That's right. I have found places for your children, ma'am. Are these the ones? This is the oldest? Well, we'll send him to a juvenile house of correction.

JENARO. What's that, Commissioner?

COMMISSIONER. There he'll learn a trade and become a useful citizen. For the rest, I've arranged places in an orphan asylum.

INDALECIA. Asylum? For my children?

COMMISSIONER. Yes, ma'am. It's all fixed up. The Welfare Society will handle every detail.

INDALECIA. My children? No, sir. Nothing like that! They're mine and they're good children.

COMMISSIONER. But, ma'am, you must understand that in cases like this——

INDALECIA. My children! I should say not! I should say not! I wouldn't think of it!

JENARO. Of course not! She's quite right.

COMMISSIONER. No one asked you. You have nothing to do with it.

JENARO. I have nothing to do with it, but I tell the truth, you see.

COMMISSIONER. Clear out, I tell you.

JENARO. Very well, but—But it's an injustice. What brutes!

REPORTER. You'll have to make up your mind to it, ma'am. Naturally it's hard to part with them, but it's preferable that the community look after them, instead of having them cause trouble later.

INDALECIA. You're probably right, but I can't give them up.

SOLDIER. Indalecia, what an idea! The first time the country has thought about rewarding an old veteran by looking after his grandchildren, and you object. Don't be so ungrateful, girl. Look, friend. I lost this arm at the Battle of Estero Bellaco, and I've got a bullet in this leg, too. And you see what I've got out of it! That my children and my grandchildren are in want. Now they are being remembered. Fine! One must take advantage of this offer. Better late than never, I say. What do you think?

COMMISSIONER. That's right. So, ma'am, make up your mind.

INDALECIA. No, sir. My mind is made up. I'll not give up my children. I can't. I never can.

SOLDIER. Nonsense! You stupid woman! You don't seem to be a daughter of mine.

COMMISSIONER. Would you prefer to see them die of hunger or turn into criminals?

INDALECIA. Of course not. You've already helped me find a room. Now help me get some work, if you will, because I'm strong, and I'll see to bringing them up and educating them.

JENARO. Spoken like a true mother!

COMMISSIONER. I told you not to butt in.

INDALECIA. And besides, they're not mine alone. What would I say to their father who loves them so much and got hurt trying to provide for them? What can I tell him when he comes out of the hospital? No, it's impossible. They're my children.

COMMISSIONER. As far as that's concerned, you don't need to worry. Your husband is seriously injured and he may never leave the hospital. Anyway, he'll remain paralyzed.

JENARO. What brutes!

(INDALECIA *starts to weep. Enter the* PHOTOGRAPHER.)

PHOTOGRAPHER (*to* REPORTER). Hi, friend!

REPORTER. Come for a shot?

PHOTOGRAPHER. Yes, looks promising. Is this the victim?

REPORTER. Do you know this gentleman? (*Making introductions*) This is the Police Commissioner. The photographer. (*They shake hands.*)

PHOTOGRAPHER. I came at just the right moment. (*To his* ASSISTANT) Here, get the camera out, and hurry. (*To the* COMMISSIONER) What a sight, eh?

COMMISSIONER. You see this everywhere. It's barbarous to think of all this misery.

PHOTOGRAPHER (*setting up tripod and camera in the midst of the crowd, and studying the light*). That's fine! (*Everybody tries to crowd in front of the camera, to get into the picture.*) We'll take one like this of her crying. That's a fine view. (*He focuses.*) The rest of you, get back. (*To the* SOLDIER) You, too, get back, please.

SOLDIER. I'm her father. Why should I get back?

PHOTOGRAPHER. All right. Excuse me. (*As soon as he turns, they crowd in again.*) Get back, I tell you.

COMMISSIONER. Look here, clear out!

PHOTOGRAPHER. Your turn will come. Don't worry. Hold that. Don't move. Just an instant. Fine!

SOLDIER. How was my picture?

PHOTOGRAPHER. Excellent. (*To the* COMMISSIONER) Now will you please come closer. And if the lady will raise her head. Please, ma'am.

JENARO. Put me in jail or do what you like, but I think this is barbarous. To evict her! And now this. What brutes! Leave that poor woman alone, confound it!

REPORTER (*to the* COMMISSIONER, *who is about to interfere*). He's right. It would be better.

PHOTOGRAPHER. As far as I'm concerned, I've got my shot. (*Starts packing up his equipment.*)

SOLDIER. Just look at that foreigner, who thinks he's one of the family. That's all we needed, confound it!

COMMISSIONER (*to* INDALECIA). Very well, ma'am, don't worry anymore. Just make up your mind to . . .

JENARO. Leave her alone. If she won't be convinced . . .

INDALECIA. My poor children! Impossible! I can't. I'd die.

REPORTER. You're being selfish. Right now, maybe, you can look after them if you work. But maybe tomorrow you can't give them food. You may get sick, or die. Then what will become of them? You won't lose anything by surrendering them to the asylum. You can visit them often. There they'll grow up. They'll learn a trade . . .

COMMISSIONER. And tomorrow they'll be useful people for you and the nation.

SOLDIER. That's right. Would you prefer seeing them in jail as criminals?

INDALECIA. All right. All right. Do whatever you want. Oh, my poor children.

COMMISSIONER. Now you're talking sense. Fine! With the money, rent a comfortable place, and tomorrow you and the children are to come to the police station and we'll all go to the asylum.

REPORTER. Come on. Good-by, ma'am. Don't worry. Be reasonable.

SOLDIER. Tell them thank you and good-by.

REPORTER. Let her alone. Any other money that comes in, we'll send by the Commissioner. (*To the* PHOTOGRAPHER) Coming?

PHOTOGRAPHER. Sure! Why not? Good afternoon, everybody.

COMMISSIONER (*to* JENARO). And you watch out. Don't go filling her with any foolish ideas.

(JENARO *turns his back.*)

SOLDIER (*to the* COMMISSIONER). Tell me, sir, have you some loose coins for an old soldier?

COMMISSIONER. To get drunk, I suppose.

SOLDIER. What do you think? That's the only thing my country ever gave me: a vice.

COMMISSIONER (*laughing*). You're right. (*He goes out, followed by the children. The neighbors are the last to go.*)

SOLDIER (*to* INDALECIA). Well, darling daughter, I haven't had much to eat today. How about giving me a little of what they gave you?

INDALECIA. Here, take it all. What use is it to me now? (*She sobs as she embraces her children.*)

CURTAIN

Translated by Willis Knapp Jones

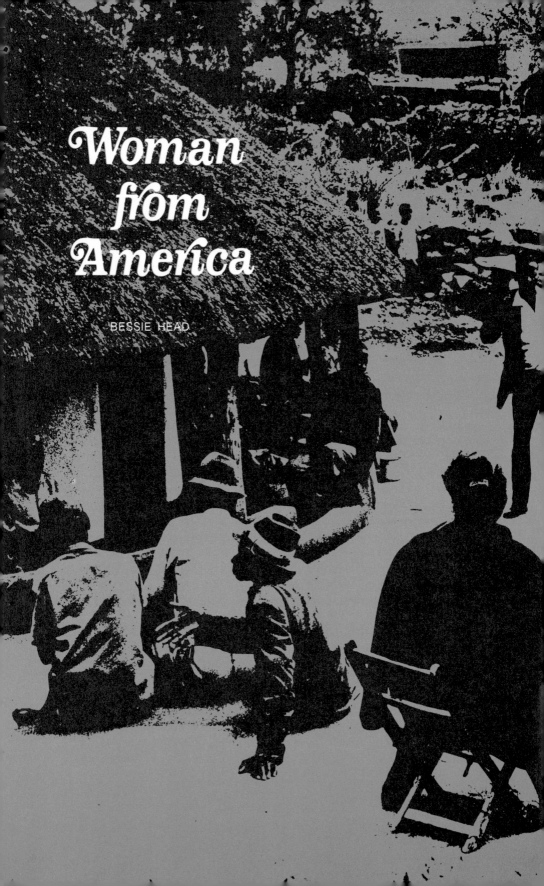

Woman
from
America

BESSIE HEAD

This woman from America married a man of our village and left her country to come and live with him here. She descended on us like an avalanche. People are divided into two camps: those who feel a fascinated love and those who fear a new thing.

Some people keep hoping she will go away one day, but already her big strong stride has worn the pathways of the village flat. She is everywhere about because she is a woman, resolved and unshakable in herself. To make matters worse or more disturbing she comes from the west side of America, somewhere near California. I gather from her conversation that people from the West are stranger than most people.

People of the West of America must be the most oddly beautiful people in the world; at least this woman from the West is the most oddly beautiful person I have ever seen. Every crosscurrent of the earth seems to have stopped in her and blended into an amazing harmony. She has a big dash of Africa, a dash of Germany, some Cherokee and heaven knows what else. Her feet are big and her body is as tall and straight and strong as a mountain tree. Her neck curves up high and her thick black hair cascades down her back like a wild and tormented stream. I cannot understand her eyes though, except that they are big, black, and startled like those of a wild free buck racing against the wind. Often they cloud over with a deep, intense, brooding look.

It takes a great deal of courage to become friends with a woman like that. Like everyone here, I am timid and subdued. Authority, everything can subdue me; not because I like it that way but because authority carries the weight of an age pressing down on life. It is terrible then to associate with a person who can shout authority down. Her shouting matches with authority are the terror and sensation of the village. It has come down to this. Either the woman is unreasonable or authority is unreasonable, and everyone in his heart would like to admit that authority is unreasonable. In reality, the rule is: If authority does not like you, then you are the outcast and humanity associates with you at their peril. So try always to be on the right side of authority, for the sake of peace, and please avoid the outcast. I do not say it will be like this forever. The whole world is crashing and interchanging itself and even remote bush villages in Africa are not to be left out!

It was inevitable though that this woman and I should be friends. I have an overwhelming curiosity that I cannot keep within bounds. I passed by the house for almost a month, but one cannot crash in on people. Then one day a dog they own had puppies, and my small son chased one of the puppies into the yard and I chased after him. Then one of the puppies became his and there had to be discussions about the puppy, the desert heat, and the state of the world and as a result of curiosity an avalanche of wealth has descended on my life. My small hut-house is full of short notes written in a wide sprawling hand. I have kept them all because they are a statement of human generosity and the wild carefree laugh of a woman who is as busy as women the world over about things women always entangle themselves in—a man, a home... Like this...

"Have you an onion to spare? It's very quiet here this morning and I'm all fagged out from sweeping and cleaning the yard, shaking blankets, cooking, fetching water, bathing children, and there's still the floor inside to sweep and dishes to wash... it's endless!"

Sometimes too, conversations get all tangled up and the African night creeps all about and the candles are not lit and the conversation gets more entangled, intense; and the children fall asleep on the floor dazed by it all.

She is a new kind of American or even maybe will be a new kind of African. There isn't anyone here who does not admire her. To come from a world of chicken, hamburgers, TV, escalators, and whatnot to a village mud hut and a life so tough, where the most you can afford to eat is ground millet and boiled meat. Sometimes you cannot afford to eat at all. Always you have to trudge miles for a bucket of water and carry it home on your head. And to do all this with loud, ringing, sprawling laughter?

Black people in America care about Africa, and she has come here on her own as an expression of that love and concern. Through her, too, one is filled with wonder for a country that breeds individuals about whom, without and within, rushes the wind of freedom. I have to make myself clear, though. She is a different person who has taken by force what America will not give black people.

The woman from America loves both Africa and America, independently. She can take what she wants from both and say, "Dammit." It is a most strenuous and difficult thing to do.

Ordinary Love Song

FLAVIEN RANAIVO

Do not love me, darling,
like your shadow
for shadows fade at dusk
and I must hold you
right on through till dawn;
nor like pepper
which makes our belly warm
for then I could not
save some for my hunger;
nor like pillows
for we'd be together in the hours of sleep
but scarcely meet by day;
nor like rice
for once consumed you'd think no more about it;
nor like endearing words
for they vanish like the mist;
nor like honey,
sweet indeed but too familiar.

Love me like a dazzling dream,
your life by night,
my hope by day;
like a silver coin,
forever with me on earth,
and a loyal companion in the mighty journey;
like a flawless gourd for drawing water,
bit by bit, as the frets for my guitar.

Translated by Julio de la Torre

MY VOICE

JUAN RAMÓN JIMÉNEZ

Sing, sing, voice of mine,
While there is something
You have not said,
You have said nothing at all.

Translated by H. R. Hays

Index of Authors and Titles